PRINCIPLE LABO
PRACTICES FOR
MICROBIOLOGY

Carolyn Caudle, Ph.D.

Joshua Ohair, Ph.D.

Kendall Hunt
publishing company

Cover image © Shutterstock.com

www.kendallhunt.com
Send all inquiries to:
4050 Westmark Drive
Dubuque, IA 52004-1840

Published in the United States of America

Contents

LAB 1

Lab Safety

General laboratory rules and regulations

1. ⌐ Never eat or drink anything in the microbiology lab.
2. Store all books, purses, and so on, under your lab bench. Only your laboratory notebook should be on the bench. Coats are to be hung on the back of your chair.
3. Never take cultures out of the laboratory.
4. Before each laboratory, read over the exercise to be done and plan to work accordingly.
5. Do not begin work until you have received instructions. Ask questions when you do not understand.
6. Properly record all observations at the times they are made in your lab notebook. Lab exams will cover this basic material and the information covered by your instructor.
7. Keep loose hair tied back and avoid wearing loose-fitting clothing and jewelry. Always be careful of the flames from the burners. Wear covered-toed shoes to class. ⌐[1]
8. ⌐ Wipe off the top of your lab station with the cleaning solution provided at the beginning of each laboratory experiment.
9. At the end of each laboratory experiment, wash your hands with soap and water located in the back of the classroom.
10. Place all exhausted or contaminated cultures in the designated areas throughout the lab.
11. If spills of live cultures occur, notify the instructor immediately. Do not attempt to clean the area by yourself.
12. Place any contaminated sharps or broken glass into the appropriate sharps containers.
13. Report any accidents immediately to your instructor. Take precautions to avoid accidents.
14. Note locations of emergency eyewash stations, emergency showers, fire extinguishers, and fire alarms. ⌐[2]

Please sign if you have read, understand, and agree to all laboratory rules.

I, the undersigned, have read the Rules of the Laboratory, and I understand them.

Name (printed) _____

Date _____

Signature _____
(sign here)

Get to know your lab

@ Trueffelpix/shutterstock.com

It will become apparent to you that some microorganisms are hazardous whereas others are not. You also will realize that some of the hazardous or pathogenic organisms are more virulent than other pathogenic organisms. For instance, the rhinovirus causes a less severe respiratory disease than the common cold, but the SARS-CoV-2 virus is much more virulent than either of these. It is because of these differences in the disease potential of microorganisms, we use different practices when working with organisms in the laboratory. Of course, we use standard microbiological techniques when working with any microorganism, but we use more precautionary techniques when working with hazardous organisms.

In this lab, the safety level is deemed **Biosafety level 1 (BSL-1)**. BSL-1 organisms are not known to cause disease in the healthy adult human. All the organisms that the students work within this laboratory are classified as BSL-1 organisms. ⌐ Examples include nonpathogenic *Escherichia coli (E. Coli)* and *Staphylococcus aureus*. Standard microbiological procedures must be carried out when using level 1 organisms. These organisms may be used on the open bench: hence, no special barriers are recommended. A sink is required for students to wash their hands after handling living organisms, and before leaving the lab. ⌐[1]

Glove use with BSL-1 organisms. Wear gloves if your hands have fresh cuts or abrasions. Gloves are not required for standard lab procedures if proper hand hygiene is performed. Proper hand hygiene involves thorough hand washing prior to and immediately after finishing handling microorganisms and anytime that microbes accidentally contact the skin.

Exercise 1: Lab Safety

Take 5 minutes and familiarize yourself with laboratory safety

Take some time now and familiarize yourself with all the safety equipment around the room. In the following square, visualize yourself sitting in the classroom. Where are the following items located? (Write them in the following square where they are in the room):

@ ThanasStudio/shutterstock.com

    Fire extinguisher

    The shower

    The eyewash

    The first aid kit in the laboratory

    The instructor

    Hazardous waste bins

    Regular trash bin

    Sharps/broken glass container

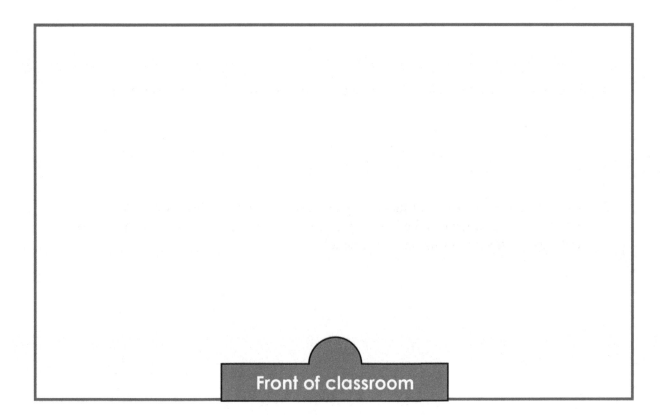

Front of classroom

Questions

1. What should a student do if a glass test tube containing only water is dropped and the glass breaks?

2. If live cultures are spilled on a student's notebook or personal items, what is the correct course of action?

3. Explain why normal trash (papers, towels, etc.) that has not come into contact with laboratory specimens does not get placed in hazardous waste labeled bins.

4. Explain how a lab benchtop should be cleaned prior to starting an experiment.

5. After you have finished your laboratory exercises for the day, briefly state how to clean your station. Also, what is the best way to eliminate microorganisms that may have contacted your skin during an experiment?

NAME ____ *LAB SECTION* ______

EMERGENCY INFORMATION

Name ____

Local Address ____

T #____

Telephone #____

Person to contact in case of emergency

Name ____

Telephone # ____

Endnotes

1. Adapted from *Techniques of Microbiology: A Laboratory Manual*, by Deborah A. Polayes. Copyright © 2021 by Kendall Hunt Publishing Company. Reprinted by permission.

2. Adapted from *Laboratory Exercises in Microbiology,* by Keith E. Belcher. Copyright © 2012 by Kendall Hunt Publishing Company. Reprinted by permission.

LAB 2

Microscope Care and Use

© Zalina Khubetsova/shutterstock.com

The simple bright-field microscope is one in which light is projected directly into the lens system to produce a field of view with a bright background. It is the most common microscope in use. Although you are probably familiar with this type of microscope, you will need to acquire good microscopic techniques in order to be successful in microbiology class. A review of the principles and practices is provided in this exercise.

There are two eyepieces or oculars to look through. These will need to be adjusted so that you can look through both oculars at the same time. The oculars fit into the body tube of the microscope. The microscope is carried by grasping the arm, a support to which the body tube is attached, as well as by placing a hand at the bottom of the microscope. Do NOT carry the microscope with only one hand.

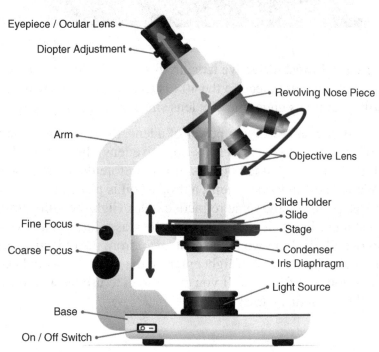

MICROSCOPE DIAGRAM

- Eyepiece / Ocular Lens
- Diopter Adjustment
- Revolving Nose Piece
- Arm
- Objective Lens
- Slide Holder
- Slide
- Fine Focus
- Stage
- Coarse Focus
- Condenser
- Iris Diaphragm
- Light Source
- Base
- On / Off Switch

© VectorMine/Shutterstock.com

At the base of the body tube, you will find the revolving nosepiece that allows rotation of the attached objective lenses. The objective lenses we will use in this class 10×, 40×, and 100×.

⌐ A mechanical slide holding mechanism is attached to the stage. There is a hole in the center of the stage to allow light to pass through the specimen when it is placed over the hole. At the base of the microscope is a large knob that moves the stage up and down so that slides can be placed on the stage. This coarse adjustment knob is also used in the initial focusing of a specimen. The fine adjustment knob is the smaller inner knob and moves the stage minimally, to accomplish fine focusing. ⌐[1] By your left hand is another knob located under the stage that raises and lowers the condenser. The condenser is a lens that concentrates the light before it reaches the specimen. An iris diaphragm is incorporated into the base of the condenser. A lever in the front of the iris diaphragm regulates the amount of light that enters the condenser from the underlying built-in light source.

Which Objective Lens Should I Use?

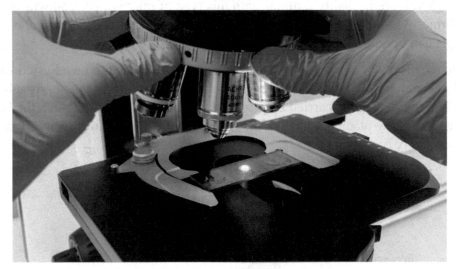

@ Prrrettty/shutterstock.com

Always start off with the lowest objective lens. In this case that is the 10×. Once your specimen is in focus, turn the nose piece so the 40× is right over the viewing area. Your specimen should still be in focus under the 40× lens since we are using parfocal objectives.

⌐ The higher the magnifying and resolving power of a lens, the more light that is required to see the specimen. The oil-immersion lens has (100× objective lens) the best resolving power and is the lens of choice for viewing very small objects. It is therefore the microscope lens required to examine bacteria. With the oil-immersion lens, a drop of oil is placed between the microscope slide and the objective. ⌐[1] Oil has the same refractive index (light-bending power) as glass and thus light flows in a straight line as it passes through the glass slide, then through the oil into the objective.⌐ Without oil, the light would be bent away from the objective as it passes from the glass slide into the air. The amount of light entering the objective would decrease and the resolution would be seriously affected. ⌐[1] If you ever forget to use oil with the oil-immersion objective, all you will see is a fuzzy image.

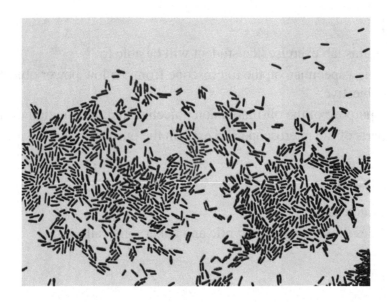

Bacillus cereus gram-stain viewed with 100× objective lens and immersion oil

© Satirus/Shutterstock.com

Total Magnification

⌐ Look at the engravings on the **eyepiece** and **objective lens** and note the magnification each provides. The magnification number is followed by an × (e.g., a 5× lens provides a fivefold magnification). ⌐[1] To calculate the **total magnification**, multiply the objective magnification times the eyepiece magnification.

Eyepiece (10× magnification) × Objective lens (100× magnification = Total Magnification 1,000×

Exercise 2: Microscope Care and Use

@ luchschenF/shutterstock.com

In today's exercise, you will use the bright-field microscope to examine prepared slides that will introduce you to the major categories of microorganisms as well as introduce you to the important features of a compound microscope.

Objective(s)

Upon completion of this lab exercise, the student will be able to:

1. Properly focus a specimen on the microscope from the low power objective to the oil-immersion objective.
2. Explain the purpose of the oil-immersion objective and the function of immersion oil.
3. Name the parts of the microscope and explain the purpose of each part.

Materials Needed

Compound microscope
Prepared slides illustrating prokaryotic and eukaryotic cells
Lens paper
Immersion oil

Procedure

1. ⌐ Begin by taking the microscope out of the cabinet using both hands—one hand on the base of the microscope and the other hand around the neck/arm of the microscope.
2. Plug in the microscope and turn it on using the on/off switch at the front of the base of the microscope.
3. Adjust the light level using the light intensity knob near the microscope base.
4. Adjust the condenser so that the lens would just touch the bottom of the slide and back off about 1/4 turn.
5. Open the iris diaphragm using the sliding lever in the front of the condenser to adjust the amount of light passing through the specimen.
6. Now you're ready to look through the oculars. Adjust the distance between the oculars so that the field changes from two circular fields to one large circular field when both eyes look into the oculars.
7. Adjust the level of the stage so that the slide may be placed on it.
8. Adjust the objectives so that the lowest objective (10×) is directly above the specimen.
9. Obtain a prepared slide from the instructor. Place the slide on the stage and secure using the stage clips.
10. Focus the specimen using the coarse adjustment knob, then fine adjustment knob, until it is in focus.
11. Rotate the objectives so that the next objective is directly above the specimen (40×).
12. **Focus using the fine adjustment knob only** (ONLY USE THE COURSE ADJUSTMENT KNOB ON THE 10× OBJECTIVE, NEVER ONTHE HIGHER POWER OBJECTIVES).
13. Rotate the objectives so that the 40× and oil objective lens (100×) "straddle" the specimen. So that you can add 1 drop of immersion oil directly to the slide or smear.
14. Then gently rotate the immersion oil objective (100×) into place directly above the specimen. The objective must touch the oil.

15. Focus using only the fine adjustment knob.
16. When finished observing the specimen under oil immersion, remove oil from oil-immersion objective with lens paper. ⌐²

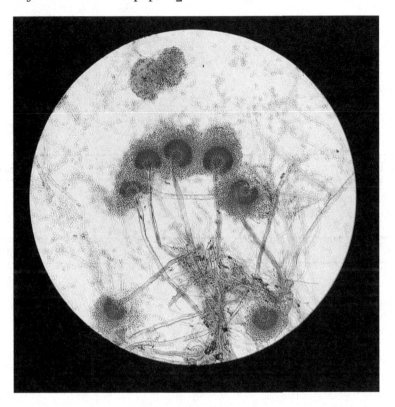

***Aspergillus terreus* under a light microscope using oil objective lens**

Results

Choose three different slides and draw your observation for each at 10×, 40×, and 100×.

Slide (1)

10×	40×	100× (using immersion oil)
Description:	Description:	Description:

Slide (2)

10×	40×	100× (using immersion oil)
Description:	Description:	Description:

Slide (3)

10×	40×	100× (using immersion oil)
Description:	Description:	Description:

Questions

1. How does the oil-immersion objective differ from the low- and high-power objectives?

2. What is the function of immersion oil?

3. What is the purpose of using the low-power objective?

4. Why is the oil-immersion objective used in microbiological studies?

5. Label the microscope using the correct term from the following word bank:
  A. Objective lens
  B. Ocular lens
  C. Stage
  D. Fine focus knob
  E. Course focus knob
  F. Oil immersion lens
  G. Light source
  H. Revolving nose piece

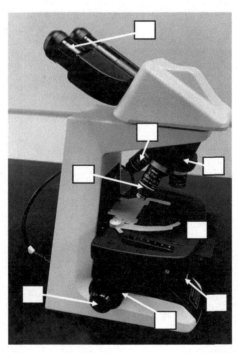

© Carolyn Caudle and Joshua Ohair/Shutterstock.com

6. What do you see as the limitations for brightfield microscopy? What other tests and instruments could be used in order to help identify unknown microorganisms?

Endnotes

1. Adapted from *Techniques of Microbiology: A Laboratory Manual*, by Deborah A. Polayes. Copyright © 2021 by Kendall Hunt Publishing Company. Reprinted by permission.

2. Adapted from *Laboratory Exercises in Microbiology,* by Keith E. Belcher. Copyright © 2012 by Kendall Hunt Publishing Company. Reprinted by permission.

LAB 3

Aseptic Transfer and Slide Preparation

©MyFavoriteTime/shutterstock.com

©NatalieIme/shutterstock.com

⌐ To handle microorganisms safely, **aseptic or sterile techniques** will be employed. These procedures permit you to sample a culture and in future experiments allow you to transfer your bacteria from one medium to another. ⌐[2] In this lab, we will use an **inoculating loop** to transfer bacteria from one media to another location. Please read the following step-by-step instructions to aseptically transfer your cultures.

The Aseptic Transfer Method

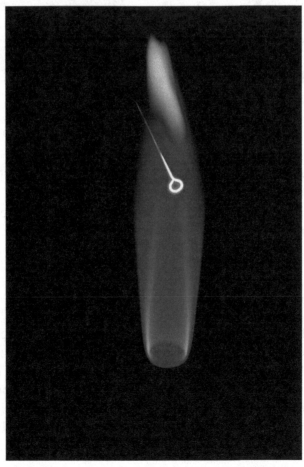

©GDuque/shutterstock.com

1. Turn the gas on for your Bunsen burner. Take the striker and strike the flint over the top ⌐ of the Bunsen burner to ignite the gas. Adjust the height of the flame and amount of oxygen to get a small arrowhead-shaped flame (pro tip: the blue part is the hottest).

2. The transfer procedure begins by flaming the inoculating loop until it is red-hot and allowing 15 seconds of cooling time.

3. The culture tube containing the organisms that are to be cultured is picked up by the other hand, and the cap or plug is removed. Keep the cap or plug in the crook of the little finger of the right hand (hand holding inoculating loop) until time to replace it on the tube. **Never lay a cap on the table, as this would serve to contaminate the culture.**

4. The neck of the tube is then flamed in the burner once or twice to destroy any unwanted organisms. ⌐[1]

5. The sterilized loop is then inserted into the tube and a small amount of the microbial growth is removed.

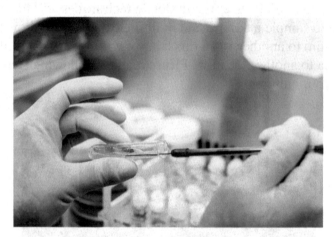

©Master the moment/shutterstock.com

6. Upon removal of the loop the neck of the tube is flamed once again and immediately recapped and placed into the test tube rack.

7. Now, your one loopful containing your specimen can be deposited to the center of a slide, into new culture media, or zone 1 of a streak plate.

8. Once this is completed, the inoculation loop is heated until it is red-hot once again to destroy any remaining growth left over.

Slide Preparation: Creating a Smear

Once you have mastered the aseptic transfer technique, bacterial specimens can now be prepared in several ways. One method, a smear, employs a small amount of cell suspension that is placed onto a microscope slide. After the liquid has air-dried, the slide is gently heated to cause the microbe in the smear to stick to the slide. ⌐ This process of **heat-fixing** prevents the microbe from being washed off the slide during the staining procedure that uses liquid dyes. ⌐[2] Heat-fixing kills the microorganism and causes changes in the bacterial cells that causes them to stain better. Follow the steps given in the following to become a smearing genius!

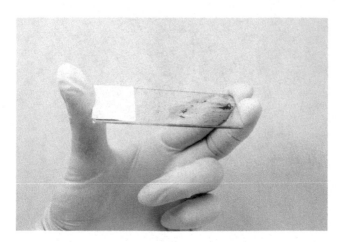

©Pongsak A/shutterstock.com

1. ⌐ Place your slide on the rods of your staining tray.
2. Follow the instructions for aseptic transfer (steps 1–8) ⌐[1]
3. Today, you will make a smear from a broth culture (liquid). The two cultures used in **LAB 3** are *Bacillus* and *Staphylococcus*. Take two or three loopful of the culture and place each loopful on the slide (pro tip: use the wax pencil to draw a circle on the opposite side of the slide so you know where you placed your loops of bacteria).
4. Let the smear has air-dry for at least 2– 3 minutes or until no more liquid is present on the slide.
5. Take hold of the end of the slide with a clothespin and heat-fix the organisms by passing the slide through the Bunsen burner flame two or three times. Quickly move the glass slide through the fame, DO NOT HOLD IT IN THE FLAME, EXCESS HEAT WILL DISTORT THE CELLS!
6. Place the heat-fixed slide back on the rods of your staining rack and apply appropriate staining dye in **LAB 4.**

Things to Know!!! IMPORTANT

Types of Media for Growing, Storing, and Transporting Bacteria

In **LAB 3,** we are working with liquid media and glass microscope slides. However, it is important to know all the types of media we will use throughout the semester. Please take some time and go over the important lab terminology as follows:

A **STOCK** culture of an organism is a culture that is maintained to propagate a particular specimen. The culture will be stored typically below freezing and its use is limited to making fresh **WORKING** culture. **WORKING** cultures are what is provided at the beginning of each lab experiment.

⌐ To cultivate microorganisms, they must be provided with appropriate nutrients and moisture. This mixture is called a **culture medium**. It may be prepared in the form of a liquid called a **broth** or found in a solidified form with agar called an **agar medium**. ⌐[2] Agar media are available in a variety of forms called deeps, slants, and plates.

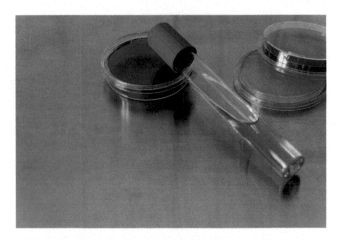

Solidified media using nutrient agar, slant (red cap test tube), and plates for growing microorganisms

© Topolszczak/Shutterstock.com

Agar is a non-nutritive polysaccharide extract derived from seaweed. It is used to solidify the medium and provide a substrate on which the organisms can grow. The agar medium is commonly provided in tubes called slants or in Petri dishes that provide a larger surface area for ⌐ growth.

Growth in broth may be detected in three different ways:

(1) **Turbidity**—a distinct cloudiness within the medium.

(2) **Pellicle formation**—a small mass or mat of cells formed on the top of the broth.

(3) **Sediment**—a deposit of cells resting at the bottom of the broth. ⌐[2]

Broth culture media with high turbidity

© Ayu Satwikha/Shutterstock.com

Exercise 3: Aseptic Transfer and Slide Preparation

In today's exercise, you will learn the appropriate steps to prepare specimens for future staining (**LAB 4**). This includes how to aseptically transfer your specimen and create a slide smear.

Objective(s)

1. To aseptically transfer specimens via inoculation loop from a broth culture.
2. Know the purpose of heat-fixing.
3. Identify the types of media used in microbiology.
4. Learn the methodology for preparing a smear.

Materials Needed

Inoculating loop
Glass microscope slides (2)
Bunsen burner and flint striker
Broth culture of *Bacillus*
Broth culture of *Staphylococcus*
Staining tray, clothespin, and wax pencil

Procedure

1. Follow the aseptic transfer protocol (steps 1–8) for each broth culture of *Bacillus* and *Staphylococcus*.
2. Follow the "Creating a Smear" protocol (steps 3–6) to prepare smears of both *Bacillus* and *Staphylococcus*.
3. Continue to **LAB 4** for simple staining and negative staining.

Results and Questions

1. By what means can growth be detected in a broth culture?

2. Describe the growth pattern in your broth tubes for your organism or unknown.

3. What is the purpose of heat-fixing and what does it do to the bacterial specimen?

4. What is the purpose of the aseptic technique? At what steps during the aseptic transfer is the inoculating loop not sterile?

Endnotes

1. Adapted from *Techniques of Microbiology: A Laboratory Manual*, by Deborah A. Polayes. Copyright © 2021 by Kendall Hunt Publishing Company. Reprinted by permission.
2. Adapted from *Laboratory Exercises in Microbiology,* by Keith E. Belcher. Copyright © 2012 by Kendall Hunt Publishing Company. Reprinted by permission.

LAB 4

Simple Staining and Negative Staining

©Sb-photography/shutterstock.com

Basic Shapes of Bacterial Cell

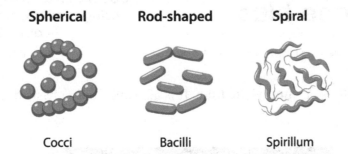

Spherical	Rod-shaped	Spiral
Cocci	Bacilli	Spirillum

Simple stains help identify morphology. The three basic shapes of bacteria are spherical, rod-shaped, and spiral

© Olga Bolbot/Shutterstock.com

To simple stain cells, we use a chemical substance called a dye. A dye, depending on its chemical properties, is placed in either of two categories: (1) **basic, direct, or positive stain** or (2) **acidic, indirect, or negative stain**. If the color of a dye is because of its positive ion, it is called a basic, direct, or positive stain. If the color is because of its negative ion component, it is called an indirect, acidic, or negative strain.

⌐Direct stains dye the cells directly because of the attraction of the charged positive dye molecule to the negatively charged cell surface. Indirect stains, on the other hand, do not dye the cell directly since the negative charge of the dye molecule repels the negative charge of the cell.⌐[1] Indirect stains then provide for a colored background against a colorless cell. In this exercise, you will stain bacterial smears using both a direct stain and an indirect stain.

QUICK TIPS   Simple staining does not differentiate between types of cells. It stains everything on the slide the same color (Differential stains such as Gram staining will be discussed later!).

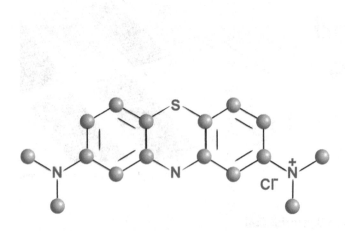

Methylene blue

©Anastasiya Litvinenka/shutterstock.com

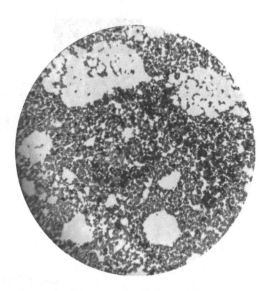

Cocci with a methylene blue stain, using a microscope with a 100x objective

© andrea_cano23/Shutterstock.com

The direct stain you will use is **methylene blue**. It is also known as a basic dye because of its positive charge.

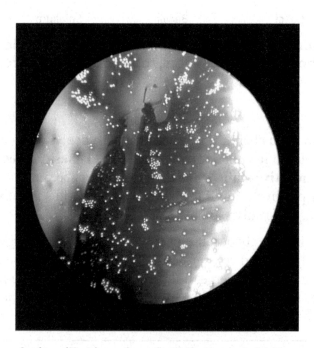

Staining of cocci bacteria with nigrosine dye. If done right the cells should look like stars in the night!

© W.C.C/Shutterstock.com

The negative stain you will use today is called **nigrosine dye**. This dye does not stain the cell as abovementioned, but is repelled by the negatively charged cell.

Exercise 4: Simple and Negative Staining

In today's exercise, you will use a simple staining technique to directly stain (methylene blue) and indirectly stain (nigrosin) bacterial cells.

Objective(s)

Upon completion of this lab exercise, the student will be able to:

1. Visualize cells stained with methylene blue using the 100 × objective lens.
2. Visualize cells stained with nigrosine using the 100 × objective lens.
3. Understand the simple staining procedure and comprehend the difference between an indirect and direct stain.

Materials Needed

Methylene dye
Nigrosine dye
Deionized (DI) water
Staining tray
Microscope slides (4)
Immersion oil
Inoculating loop
Bacterial broth cultures (*Bacillus* and *Staphylococcus*)
Blotting paper, wax pencil, and clothespin

Procedure

Part A. Direct Staining

1. ⌐From **LAB 3**, follow "aseptic transfer" and "creating a smear" protocol so you have two slides with smears prepared. (one smear of *Bacillus* and one smear of *Staphylococcus*)

2. Place the slides with the heat-fixed smear side **UP** on the staining pan and cover the smear with 5–6 drops from the dropper of Methylene blue for 30 seconds.

3. At the end of 30 seconds gently wash the slide using the wash bottles located at your station. **DO NOT WASH WITH NOZZLE DIRECTLY OVER YOUR**

©MyFavoriteTime/shutterstock.com

SMEAR, this will wash away your bacteria and clear the slide. Instead, gently wash the slide with a nozzle just above the bacterial smear and let the water flow down over your stained area. Wash for 5–10 seconds. **YOU DO NOT NEED TO WASH ALL OF THE STAIN OFF.**

4. Dry with blotting paper using a dabbing motion⌐,[2] taking care not to rub the smear off the slide.

5. Examine the slide under the oil immersion lens of the microscope (100 ×).

©Ariyaporn chumkong/shutterstock.com

Part B. Indirect Staining

1. From **LAB 3**, follow the "aseptic transfer" so you have two slides with one loopful of *Bacillus* on one slide and one loopful of *Staphylococcus* on the other slide.

2. ⌐Do not heat-fix or let the bacterial liquid dry out on the slide.

3. Add a drop of Nigrosine stain next to the drop of bacteria and mix with a sterile inoculating loop.

4. Spread to make a thin smear by using the edge of a separate glass slide starting from one end and pulling towards yourself.

5. Allow the slide to air dry⌐,[2] but DO NOT HEAT FIX.

6. Examine the preparation with the oil immersion objective of your microscope (100 ×).

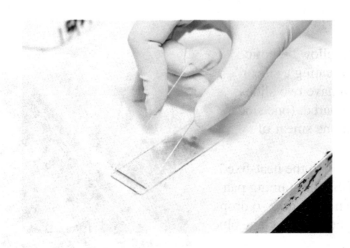

©Master the moment/shutterstock.com

Results

Draw your specimen and describe the morphology and predominant arrangement when observed with the oil immersion lens (100 ×).

Direct stain used _____

Bacillus	Staphylococcus
Description:	Description:

Indirect stain used_____

Bacillus	Staphylococcus
Description:	Description:

Questions

1. Distinguish between direct and indirect staining.

2. Why are cells fixed to the slide when using a positive/direct staining method?

3. How do cells differ when observed in positive/direct stain from those stained by the negative/indirect method?

4. What are the limitations of simple staining?

5. If your cultures of *Bacillus* and *Staphylococcus* were accidentally mixed, could you confirm this by only using simple staining techniques? How?

Endnotes

1. Adapted from *Techniques of Microbiology: A Laboratory Manual*, by Deborah A. Polayes. Copyright © 2021 by Kendall Hunt Publishing Company. Reprinted by permission.

2. Adapted from *Laboratory Exercises in Microbiology*, by Keith E. Belcher. Copyright © 2012 by Kendall Hunt Publishing Company. Reprinted by permission.

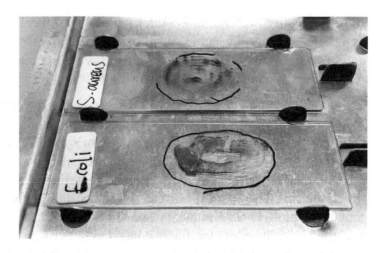

LAB 5
Gram Staining

© OneMashi/shutterstock.com

The Gram stain differentiates nearly all bacteria into two major categories: **Gram-positive** and **Gram-negative**. This is a **differential stain** that allows for the classification of bacteria into these two groups. These two groups stain differently because of differences in their cell wall structure.

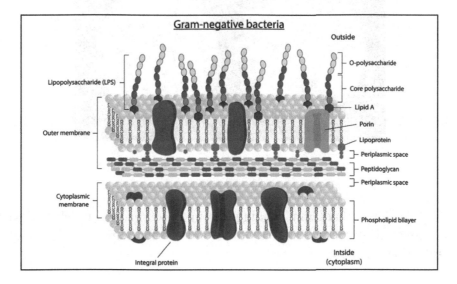

© Kallayanee Naloka/Shutterstock.com

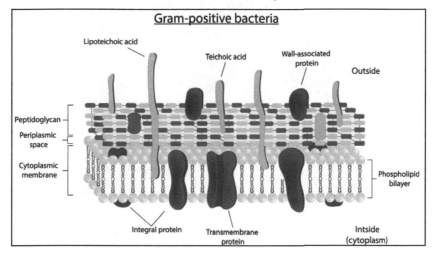

© Kallayanee Naloka/Shutterstock.com

⌐ Gram-positive bacteria have a thick single-layered cell wall made up almost entirely of a complex macromolecule called **peptidoglycan**. Most Gram-negative bacteria have a multilayered cell wall made up of a thin layer of peptidoglycan surrounded by an outer membrane called the **lipopolysaccharide** (LPS) layer.[1] ⌐

The Gram staining procedure involves first staining the cells that are fixed on a microscope slide with the dye **crystal violet**. ⌐ Both groups of cells will take up this purple-colored dye. The cells are then treated with the mordant, **Gram's iodine** (an iodine–potassium iodide solution). This dye complexes with the crystal violet to make a larger complex. Upon treatment with 95% ethanol, the cell wall of the Gram-positive bacteria becomes dehydrated, thus trapping the dye inside the cell. The Gram-positive cells are resistant to the removal of the dye by the ethanol and remain purple. The 95% ethanol dissolves the outer LPS of Gram-negative bacteria. These cells lose the bluish-purple color and become decolorized by the ethanol.[1] ⌐ In order to visualize the Gram-negative cells, red dye **safranin** is used to counterstain the Gram-negative bacteria. Thus, when the Gram stain procedure is performed correctly, **Gram-positive cells are purple and Gram-negative cells are pink or red.**

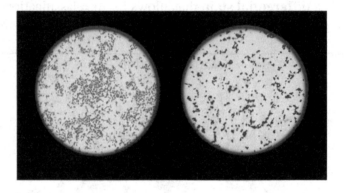

© Schira/Shutterstock.com

DID YOU KNOW?   Did you know that Gram staining was first used in 1884 by Hans Christian Gram? This procedure not only differentiates but helps provide a diagnosis with infectious bacteria.

Shapes of bacteria

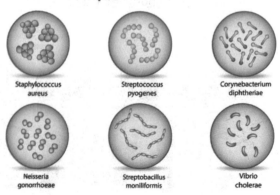

©ferryina/shutterstock.com

Exercise 5: The Gram Stain

In today's exercise, you will learn how to use the differential staining technique called the Gram stain. By the end of this lab, you should be able to carryout the staining procedure as well as visualize your specimen under the microscope with the 100x objective lens and identify the Gram reaction.

Objective(s)

1. Know the Gram staining steps and understand the purpose of using crystal violet, Gram's iodine, ethanol (95%), and safranin.
2. To be able to visualize the Gram reaction with the 100x objective lens
3. To understand why Gram-positive and Gram-negative cells stain their perspective purple and pink color.

Materials Needed

1. Broth media test tube containing *Bacillus*
2. Broth media test tube containing *E.coli*
3. Broth media test tube containing *Staph*
4. Crystal violet stain
5. Grams Iodine mordant
6. 95% Ethyl alcohol decolorizer
7. Safranin counter stain
8. Bunsen burner
9. Staining pans
10. Compound microscope
11. Microscope slides, immersion oil, inoculating loop, clothespin, and blotting paper

Procedure

1. Take three clean microscope slides (or one for each culture assigned).
2. Using the wax pencil, draw a circle on the bottom of each slide in the middle (this is where you will place your loopful of bacteria).
3. Using the aseptic technique described previously, prepare a smear for each culture on a separate slide.

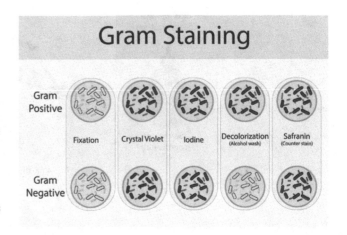

© Bass stock/Shutterstock.com

4. Allow the smears to air-dry, then heat-fix the samples.

5. **Cover** the slides with **crystal violet** and stain for 1 minute.

   1 Rinse the stain off carefully with water into the staining pan. (**pro tip:** Do not point the nozzle of wash bottle directly at bacterial smear, point the nozzle above smear and let the water run over sample area)

6. Cover the slide with **Gram's iodine** solution. Let sit for one minute, then rinse with water and drain the slide.

7. Decolorize with **95% ethanol** for **10 seconds**.

8. **Immediately rinse** with water and drain the slide.

9. Counterstain with **safranin** for 1 minute.

10. Rinse with water, drain, and blot dry using blotting paper.

11. Examine the samples under immersion oil (100x).

12. Record your observations in the Results section.

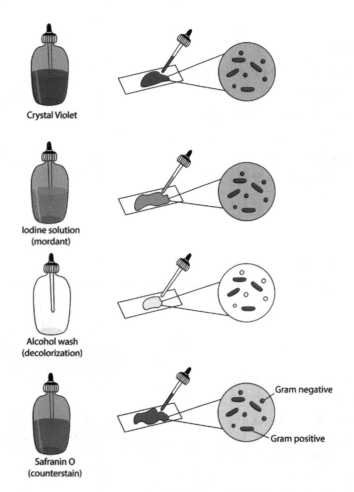

Crystal Violet

Iodine solution
(mordant)

Alcohol wash
(decolorization)

Safranin O
(counterstain)

Gram negative

Gram positive

© Kallayanee Naloka/Shutterstock.com

Troubleshooting Help

Problem	What could be the problem
Gram-positive appear pink (should be purple)	Iodine was forgotten or ethanol was left too long on slide
Gram-negative appear purple or blue	Smear was too thick, or safranin wasn't added to smear long enough
Nothing visible on the slide	Smear was not dry enough before the stain was added or excessive washing with water or microscope was not in focus

Results

Draw your observations and record details in the following.

Organism: _____

Magnification: _____

Gram Reaction: _____

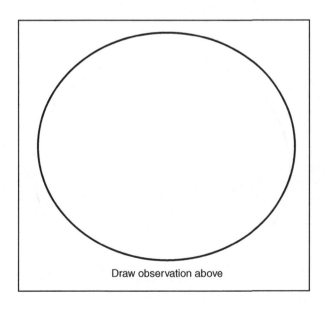

Draw observation above

Organism: _____

Magnification: _____

Gram Reaction: _____

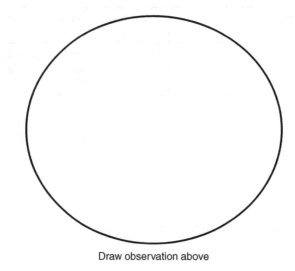

Draw observation above

Organism: _____

Magnification: _____

Gram Reaction: _____

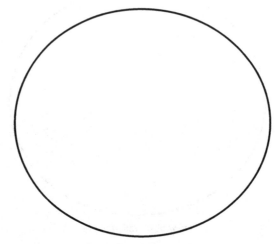

Draw observation above

Questions

1. What will be the result if the following errors occur?

    a. De-staining with ethanol for 1 minute:

    b. Smears are not dry or heat-fixed to slide

    c. Smear is prepared too thick

    d. Safranin is not added

2. You can see your cells using the 10 × objective lens. When you add oil to your slide and move to the oil immersion objective you cannot see anything. What are your options at this point to correct this?

3. Why is Gram's Iodine added in the Gram staining procedure?

4. Can you tell the type of genus and species of bacteria through Gram staining? Explain?

5. If your instructor gives you a culture of *E. coli* and you perform the Gram stain and the Gram reaction turns out to be positive, did you achieve the correct result? If not, what might have you done wrong?

Endnotes

1. Adapted from *Techniques of Microbiology: A Laboratory Manual*, by Deborah A. Polayes. Copyright © 2021 by Kendall Hunt Publishing Company. Reprinted by permission.

LAB 6

Acid-Fast and Endospore Staining

© Saiful52/shutterstock.com

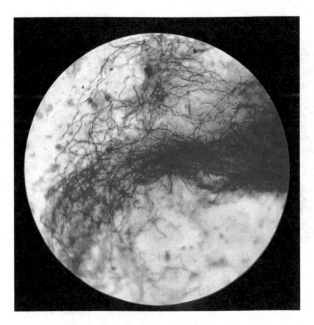

Red branching *mycobacterium tuberculosis* in acid-fast staining

© Schira/Shutterstock.com

This differential stain was first used to identify *Mycobacterium tuberculosis*, the organism responsible for the disease tuberculosis. The acid-fast stain receives its name because ***Mycobacterium tuberculosis*** and other Mycobacteria have a tendency to resist decolorization by acids. This is because of the high content of fat or waxy lipid called **mycolic acid** in their cell walls. We will be using the Ziehl–Neelsen procedure with the Kinyoun modification to correctly identify acid-fast staining bacteria in the lab. In this procedure, we will use **carbolfuchsin** that has a high affinity for mycolic acid. Once cells are stained with carbolfuchsin, an acid–alcohol mixture is added to decolorize nonacid fast staining bacteria. Those with mycolic acid will retain the carbolfuchsin dye and stain a **reddish pink**. Finally, methylene blue is added as a counterstain that will dye all nonacid fast cells blue.

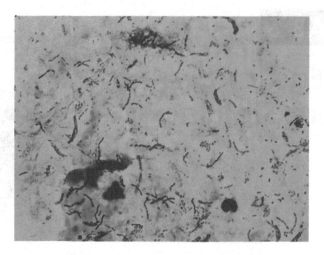

© Pingpoy/shutterstock.com

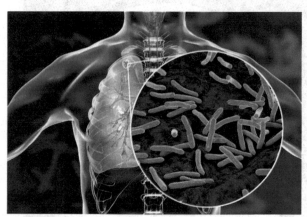

Secondary tuberculosis in lungs and close-up view of *Mycobacterium tuberculosis*

© Kateryna Kon/Shutterstock.com

Stages of Endospore Formation

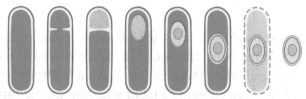

Stages of endospore formation: cell division, engulfment of prespore, formation cortex, coat, maturation of spore, and cell lysis

© Olga Bolbot/Shutterstock.com

In our second differential stain, we will stain **endospores**, a structural component belonging to species of the genera Bacillus, Clostridium, and Sporosarcina. The endospore is a highly resistant body capable of surviving long periods of extremely harsh conditions. Endospores are formed when nutrients run out or conditions have become intolerable by the cell. These "escape pods" can remain dormant for long periods of time and can become new cells again once the growth conditions are favorable. Endospores are a major reason for **autoclaving**, a sterilization technique that uses increased pressure to reach temperatures of 121°C for at least 15–20 minutes. Endospores are virtually indestructible but temperatures this high can break down the outer-spore coat. In this portion of the lab exercise, you will prepare an endospore stain using the dye **malachite green** which will stain the endospore with the help of steam. The remaining cells will be counterstained with **safranin** (the same counterstain used in Gram staining).

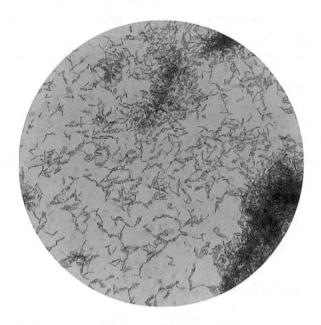

Endospore staining of the *Bacillus cereus*. Endospores stain as green and the vegetative cells as red under oil immersion lens

© Jirawan muangnak/Shutterstock.com

Did you Know?

DID YOU KNOW?

Some endospores have been found to survive over 100,000 years! fossils such as these could still harbor ancient endospores

© Ernie Cooper/Shutterstock.com

Exercise 6: Acid-Fast and Endospore Staining

For today's experiment, you will learn how to carryout both acid-fast staining and endospore staining. Both of these differential staining techniques are useful in identifying specific genera of bacteria.

Objective(s)

1. To learn how to stain acid-fast organisms and understand the dyes involved.
2. To learn how to stain endospores and understand the dyes involved as well as the reasoning for using steam.
3. To understand why differential stains are used to help classify pathogens.

Materials Needed

1. Test tube containing broth culture of *Mycobacterium smegmatis*
2. Test tube containing broth culture of *E. coli*
3. Test tube containing broth culture of spore-forming *Bacillus subtilis*
4. Carbolfuchsin dye
5. Methylene blue dye
6. Malachite green dye
7. Safranin dye
8. Bunsen burner
9. 500-mL beaker filled with 300 mL of water
10. Paper towels
11. Staining pans
12. Compound microscope
13. Microscope slides, immersion oil, inoculating loop, clothespin, and blotting paper

Procedure

Part 1: Acid-fast staining

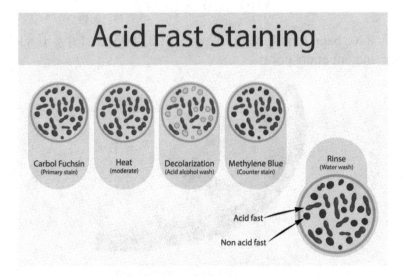

© Bass stock/Shutterstock.com

1. Using the aseptic transfer technique from previous methods, transfer 2–3 loopful of each *Mycobacterium smegmatis and E. coli* to individual slides

2. Let slides with liquid culture dry, then heat fix smears (pro tip: Remember to use a clothespin to hold slide while heat fixing)

3. Cover the smear directly with carbolfuchsin. Allow staining for 5–7 min.

4. ⌐Gently rinse off the stain with deionized water. (pro tip: only rinse for about 5 seconds, some dye may still be left)

5. Decolorize with acid alcohol for 1 minute.

6. Rinse with deionized water.

7. Repeat decolorization (acid alcohol) for 1 minute (Steps 7 and 8 are optional)

8. Rinse with deionized water.

9. Flood the smear with methylene blue counterstain.

10. Allow staining for 2 minutes.

11. Rinse off the stain with deionized water.

12. Gently blot dry.

13. Examine with oil immersion objective (100 ×)⌐[1]

Smear flooded with carbolfuchsin on a staining rack

© niphart sangpraphan/Shutterstock.com

Part 2: Endospore staining

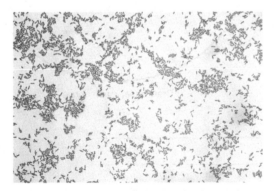

Endospore staining of Bacillus with vegetative cells staining pink

© Kallayanee Naloka/Shutterstock.com

1. Using the aseptic transfer technique from previous methods, transfer 2–3 loopful of *Bacillus* to a microscope slide.
2. Dry and heat-fix smears as you have done in the past.
3. ⌐Place the slides on a staining rack above boiling water.
4. Flood the smear with 5% Malachite green.
5. Keep the slide saturated! Do not let the smear dry while heating and continue to heat for 10 minutes. (pro tip: Add 3–4 drops of malachite green when the slide starts to look dry)
6. Remove from the heat and wash gently with deionized water.
7. Counter-stain with safranin for 30 seconds.
8. Wash with deionized water
9. Gently blot dry.
10. Examine under oil immersion for the presence of spores. (pro tip:The spores will take on a green–color whereas the cytoplasm or vegetative cell is stained pink)⌐[1]

Results

Part 1: Acid-fast staining

Draw your observations and record details in the following.

Organism: _____

Magnification: _____

Acid fast Reaction: _____

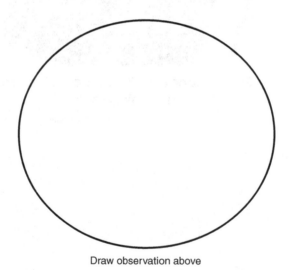

Draw observation above

Organism: _____

Magnification: _____

Acid fast Reaction: _____

NAME _____   *LAB SECTION* _____

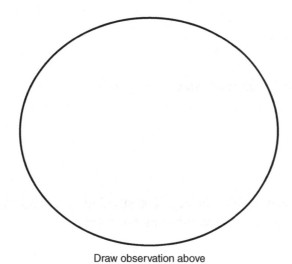

Draw observation above

Part 2: Endospore staining

Draw your observations and record details in the following.

Organism: _____

Magnification: _____

Location of spores: _____

_____

_____

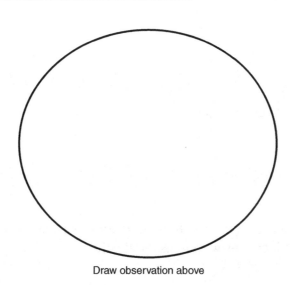

Draw observation above

Questions

1. What organisms will stain red with carbolfuchsin?

2. If no counterstain was used in the acid-fast staining procedure, what would *E. coli* look like under a microscope using an oil immersion lens?

3. If acid-fast bacteria were stained using the Gram stain procedure, what would their Gram reaction be? Why?

4. What is an endospore?

5. What genera produce endospores?

6. Describe the endospore location within the *Bacillus* species you stained. Describe three types of endospore locations within bacterial cells.

7. Based on this diagram showing the life cycle of sporulation, why would a vegetative cell enter into Stage 1?

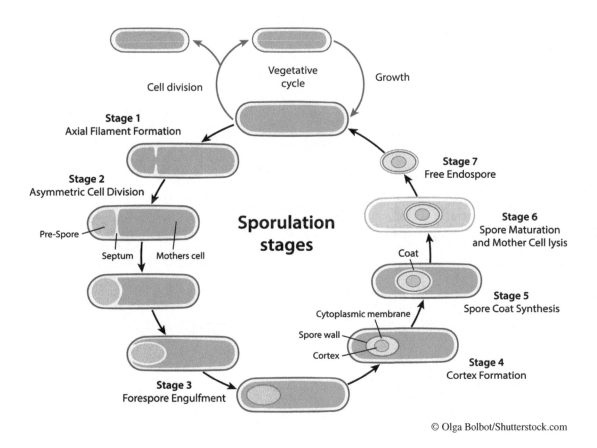

© Olga Bolbot/Shutterstock.com

Endnote

1. Adapted from *Laboratory Exercises in Microbiology,* by Keith E. Belcher. Copyright © 2012 by Kendall Hunt Publishing Company. Reprinted by permission.

LAB 7

Lab Practical

© attem/shutterstock.com

Neisseria gonorrhoeae

Tetracoccus

Sarcina

Salmonella

© ducu59us/Shutterstock.com

Unknown Specimen Identification

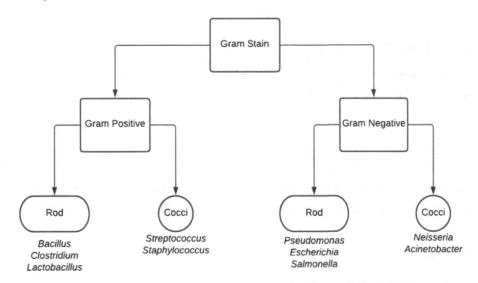

Figure 1 Diagram displaying several common Genera classified by their Gram stain reaction

© Carolyn Caudle and Joshua Ohair

⌐There are many reasons for isolating and identifying bacteria as seen in figure 1. For instance, the causative agent of an infectious disease may need to be determined to enhance the treatment of its victims. Isolation and identification of specific fermentative bacteria may result in the use of these organisms in industry. Identification of organisms involved in food production or preservation may lead to the isolation of more favorable strains of these organisms. Isolation and identification of organisms from nature allow for a better understanding of the ecosystem from which they came. Also, the identification of unknown organisms is, of course, necessary for taxonomic purposes.⌐[1]

47

Today, you will be given an organism known to us but unknown to you! For the lab practical you will determine the morphological characteristics (shape, size, and arrangement) and Gram staining reaction of the organism. Although the tests you will be doing are of a classical nature, they still give good information about your organism. Modern identification of organisms is now usually based on molecular techniques such as sequencing, but classical methods are still quicker and less expensive.

Exercise 7: Unknown Identification

In this lab practical you will be given an "unknown" culture for you to determine the Gram reaction and several other characteristics.

Objective(s)

1. To successfully carry out gram staining.
2. To successfully observe your "unknown" with the immersion-oil lens (100 ×).
3. To classify your "unknown" based on morphology, size, and arrangement.

Materials Needed

1. "Unknown" culture in broth media
2. Crystal violet stain
3. Grams Iodine mordant
4. 95% Ethyl alcohol decolorizer
5. Safranin counter stain
6. Bunsen burner
7. Staining pans
8. Compound microscope
9. Microscope slides, immersion oil, inoculating loop, clothespin, and blotting paper

LAB PRACTICAL (TEAR THIS PAGE OUT AND TURN-IN WHEN FINISHED)

Complete all following questions.

1. What is the purpose of Gram staining?

2. What other methods can be used to identify microorganisms such as bacteria?

    _____

3. Total magnification? _____

    Gram reaction? _____

    Morphology? _____

    Arrangement? _____

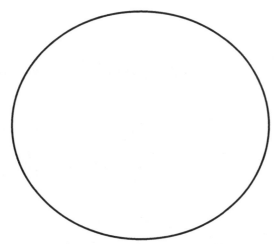

Draw observation above with 100 × lens

© Carolyn Caudle and Joshua Ohair

4. Using the Gram stain identification chart at the beginning of this lab, what genera would your organism most likely be? (Choose one)

Endnote

1. Adapted from *Techniques of Microbiology: A Laboratory Manual*, by Deborah A. Polayes. Copyright © 2021 by Kendall Hunt Publishing Company. Reprinted by permission.

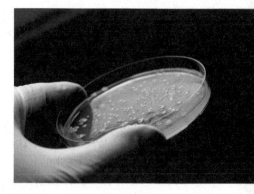

© serapyilmaz/shutterstock.com

© sruilk/shutterstock.com

LAB 8

Microbial Metabolism Part 1

Metabolism

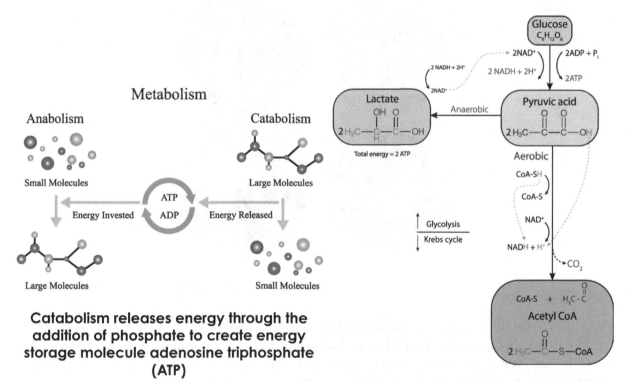

Anabolism

Small Molecules

Energy Invested

Large Molecules

Catabolism

Large Molecules

Energy Released

Small Molecules

Catabolism releases energy through the addition of phosphate to create energy storage molecule adenosine triphosphate (ATP)

© Sansanorth/Shutterstock.com

Glucose enters glycolysis and exits as pyruvate. Aerobic and Anaerobic pathways differ in both the amount of ATP generated and end product produced

© zcxes/Shutterstock.com

⌐Most microorganisms utilize glucose and or related sugars as the main source of energy. The ATP produced during the **metabolism** of glucose comes from oxidative phosphorylation or the electron transport system. Metabolism involves **enzymes**, which are proteins, that speed up chemical reactions. Macromolecules such as carbohydrates and proteins are broken down to sugar monomers and amino acids by a process called **catabolism**. The products of catabolism are determined by the pathways possessed by each genus and species of microorganism. **Biochemical assays** use various selective and differential agar plates, slants, and broths to identify the degradation of specific metabolites.⌐[1] The results from metabolic pathway testing through these assays can help determine the pathogen in an infection, unknown in a lab or identification of a new species. Today, we will be investigating metabolic pathways through the following assays.

Starch Hydrolysis

⌐Starch agar is used to check for the ability to hydrolysis starch in the medium. Starch is a complex polysaccharide that is often degraded by bacteria that produce the enzyme amylase. Iodine is added to starch plates to expose degraded starch.⌐[1] The clear zones (can look yellowish) indicate amylase production and starch degradation. Any area that stains a dark brown has intact starch and has not been degraded by enzymes.

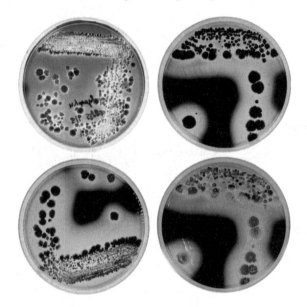

© Mallymoya/shutterstock.com

OF-Glucose

Oxidative/fermentation glucose test (OF-test) is used for the identification of fermentative or oxidative carbohydrate utilization. The original solution has a dark green color and a yellow color that indicates a positive test and production of acid from glucose. This can be observed under aerobic or anaerobic (mineral oil covering the surface of the liquid) conditions.

© OneMashi/shutterstock.com

Sugar Fermentation

The sugar fermentation test: (left) positive for acid production (yellow) and positive for gas production (bubble in Durham tube), (center) negative for acid production (red) and negative for gas production, and (right) positive for acid production and negative for gas production

Fermentation assays look for acid production from fermentation of various sugars (glucose, sucrose, lactose, etc.). If the phenol red indicator remains red, there is no acid being produced, but if a yellow color is formed, the pH has dropped below 6.8. ⌐A Durham tube (a small tube seen inside the broth liquid) is a tube that collects gas (i.e., CO_2). Air bubbles are seen in Durham tubes if gas is produced from fermentation.⌐[1]

MR-VP-Methyl Red (MR) and Voges-Proskauer (VP)

The Methyl Red (MR) test looks for a low pH (positive, red), which indicates a pH between 4.4 and 6.0.

The Voges-Proskauer (VP) test looks for acetoin (neutral end-product, pH > 6.0) through the addition of KOH and alpha-naphthol (positive, red at top of the tube near oxygen)

⌐Some organisms can hydrolyze the amino acid tryptophan into indole and pyruvic acid using the enzyme, tryptophanase. The addition of Kovac's reagent to tryptophan-containing media will result in a red product in the presence of indole. Some organisms ferment glucose first to pyruvic acid and then to other acids. These other acids produce a pH lower than 5.0. *Such a low pH cannot be detected by phenol red; therefore, another indicator, methyl red is used. At pH's above 5.0, methyl red is yellow and below 5.0, it is red.* The ability of methyl red to detect these acids is the basis of the methyl red test. Organisms producing only pyruvic acid will give a negative methyl red test and may convert the acid to 2,3-butanediol, a neutral end product. Acetyl methyl carbinol or acetoin is a precursor to butanediol and is readily detected by the addition of Barritt's reagent yielding a red color or positive VP test.⌐[1]

Citrate Test

The citrate test looks for microbes that can use citric acid as the sole carbon source. A positive test turns the media from the starting green color (negative) to a bright blue (positive).

⌜Organisms such as *Enterobacter* and *Serratia* utilize citrate as a sole carbon source. The use of Simmon's citrate agar slants is used for the detection of citrate utilization.⌟[1] The dye bromothymol blue is used as an indicator and detects a shift in pH to alkaline (green to blue) as the citrate is used.

Gelatin Hydrolysis

The gelatin test looks for bacteria that can hydrolyze the protein gelatin. A positive test for gelatinase will turn the solidified gelatin tube into a liquid (positive, top tube) (negative, bottom tube).

⌜The protein gelatin is digested by some organisms that produce the proteolytic enzyme gelatinase. Before inoculation the gelatin present in the tube causes it to be solid. In a negative test, gelatin agar remains solid; however, if gelatinase is present in the organism tested, the media will turn to a liquid in a positive test.⌟[1]

Urea Hydrolysis

The urea test looks for microorganisms that can break down. These organisms have the enzyme urease, which produces the product ammonia. A positive test will appear a pink-fuchsia color (left-tube).

⌐Some organisms, particularly those of the genus *Proteus*, produce urease, an enzyme that splits urea into ammonia and carbon dioxide. The production of ammonia will cause the pH of the system to rise; urease activity is detected by the change in the indicator from yellow to a deep pink or fuchsia⌐[1]

Exercise 8: Microbial Metabolism (Part I)

In part I of microbial metabolism, we will look at the different carbohydrate and protein assays used to identify several bacterial strains based on genus and species. After this exercise, you will know the indicators used for each assay and what a positive or negative result implies.

Objective(s)

1. Know what a positive and negative result looks like for starch hydrolysis, OF-glucose, fermentation, MR-VP, citrate, gelatin, and urea assay.
2. Understand which enzymes are important in each assay performed.
3. Be able to identify certain bacteria based on their biochemical assay results.

Materials Needed

For the following tests/assays, be sure to transfer all bacteria using sterile techniques with the inoculating loop. For agar plates and slant tubes, you will gently scrape the bacteria to the surface of the media without breaking the agar. For deep tubes, you will pierce the agar with your inoculating loop.

Starch Hydrolysis

1. Starch agar plate
2. Bacterial cultures: *Bacillus, E. coli*, and *Pseudomonas*
3. Iodine dropper (Different than Gram's Iodine Solution)

OF- Glucose

1. Six OF-Glucose tubes (green liquid tubes)
2. Bacterial cultures: *E. coli, Pseudomonas,* and *Alcaligenes*
3. Mineral oil

Sugar Fermentation

1. Four glucose (dextrose) fermentation tubes (blue caps)
2. Four lactose fermentation tubes (green caps)
3. Four sucrose fermentation tubes (yellow caps)
4. Bacterial cultures: *E. coli, Enterobacter, Alcaligenes,* and *Proteus*

MR-VP

1. Four MR-VP broth tubes (clear/yellowish liquid)
2. Bacterial cultures: *E. coli* and *Enterobacter*

Citrate

1. Three Simmons citrate slants (green agar slant tubes)
2. Bacterial cultures: *E. coli, Enterobacter, and Proteus*

Gelatin Hydrolysis

1. Four Nutrient Gelatin tubes (clear/yellowish solid deep agar tubes)
2. Bacterial cultures: *Pseudomonas, Proteus, Staph, and Bacillus*

Urea Hydrolysis

1. Four Urea agar slants (clear/yellowish agar slant tubes)
2. Cultures: *Pseudomonas, Proteus, Staph,* and *Bacillus*

Procedure(s)

Read all procedures carefully. Keep note of procedures that will be carried out on Day 1 of your experiment and Day 2 (the following lab session). For results to LAB 8, bacteria must be incubated for at least 24 hours in order to observe growth.

Starch Hydrolysis

DAY 1

1. Divide a starch agar plate into three sections like that of a pie. (pro tip: always put all writing on the bottom of the plate)
2. Using a sterile loop streak each section of the plate with the three bacteria mentioned in the materials section
3. Incubate the plates in your lab section's assigned incubator (not the fridge) for at least 24 hours

DAY 2

1. After the incubation period, flood the starch agar plate with iodine covering all bacteria
2. A positive starch will appear as a clear/yellowish area around the bacteria
3. Record your results

OF-Glucose

DAY 1

1. Inoculate two OF-Glucose tubes with *E. coli,* two tubes with *pseudomonas,* and two tubes with *Alcaligenes*

2. To one tube of *E. coli, Pseudomonas,* and *Alcaligenes* add four or five drops of mineral oil (this will create an anaerobic growth condition)

3. Incubate all tubes for at least 24 hours

DAY 2

1. After the incubation period, observe tubes for a color change (yellow is a positive result, green is a negative result)

2. Record your results

Sugar Fermentation

DAY 1

1. Label tubes for each bacterium in the following, and inoculate each into the three types of fermentation media in the following. You should have a total of 12 tubes (4 glucose, 4 lactose, and 4 sucrose).

E. coli into the tubes below	*Enterobacter* into the tubes below	*Alcaligenes* into the tubes below	*Proteus* into the tubes below
Glucose	Glucose	Glucose	Glucose
Lactose	Lactose	Lactose	Lactose
Sucrose	Sucrose	Sucrose	Sucrose

2. Incubate the tubes at 37°C for at least 24 hours and read the results next week.

DAY 2

1. Record results from glucose, lactose, and sucrose tubes for each bacterium.

MR-VP

DAY 1

1. Obtain bacterial cultures: *E. coli* and *Enterobacter* and place each into two tubes of MR-VP media. (You will need four tubes of MR-VP media total, two for *E. coli,* and two for *Enterobacter*)

2. Incubate the four tubes for at least 48 h in an incubator at 37°C.

DAY 2

1. After incubation, for one tube of *E. coli* and one tube of *Enterobacter* add 5 drops of methyl red. (pro tip: A red color indicates a positive methyl red test.)

2. For the other two tubes, add 12 drops of VP reagent I and three drops of VP reagent II.

3. Cover with parafilm and shake the tubes.

4. Remove the parafilm and allow the tubes to stand for 15–30 min. (pro tip: A positive VP test will be pinkish to red.)

Citrate

DAY 1

1. Use bacterial cultures: *E. coli, Enterobacter*, and *Proteus* for the citrate test
2. Using an inoculating loop streak the slants with the bacteria cultures.
3. Incubate the tubes for 48 hours at 37°C

DAY 2

1. Read the results. (A positive for citrate utilization will result in blue color)

Gelatin Hydrolysis

DAY 1

1. Obtain four nutrient gelatin tubes
2. Label each tube with the names of the bacterial cultures: *Pseudomonas, Proteus, Staph*, and *Bacillus*
3. Inoculate the gelatin tubes with the bacteria by piercing the hard agar and touching the bottom of the tube with the inoculating loop
4. Incubate for 2–4 days in an incubator at 37°C

DAY 2

1. Record results. (A positive test will result in the gelatin being liquefied.)

Urea Hydrolysis

DAY 1

1. Obtain four urea agar slant tubes
2. Inoculate the following cultures: *Pseudomonas, Proteus, Staph*, and *Bacillus* into each tube.
3. Incubate the tubes for 24–48 hours at 37°C

DAY 2

1. Read the results. (A positive test will turn a fuchsia-pink)

Results

Starch Hydrolysis

Organism	Growth (yes or no)	Color of medium around colonies (after adding iodine)	Starch Hydrolysis (yes or no)
Bacillus			
E. Coli			
Pseudomonas			

OF-Glucose

Organism	Growth		Color		Fermenter or Oxidative
	Aerobic tube	Anaerobic tube (w/mineral oil)	Aerobic tube	Anaerobic tube (w/mineral oil)	
Pseudomonas					
Alcaligenes					
E. coli					

Sugar Fermentation

Organism	Carbohydrate											
	Glucose				Lactose				Sucrose			
	Growth	Color	Acid	Gas	Growth	Color	Acid	Gas	Growth	Color	Acid	Gas
E. coli												
Enterobacter												
Alcaligenes												
Proteus												

MR-VP

Organism	Growth	MR		VP	
	Yes or No	Color	+ or -	Color	+ or -
E. coli					
Enterobacter					

Citrate

Organism	Growth	Color	+ or -
E. coli			
Enterobacter			

Gelatin Hydrolysis and Urea Hydrolysis

	Results				
	Pseudomonas		*Proteus*		
	Growth	Hydrolysis (+ or -)	Growth	Hydrolysis (+ or -)	Color
Gelatin Test					
Urease Test					

Questions

1. Identify two major acids produced by bacteria. Name one major gas produced as a by-product of carbohydrate metabolism?

2. What is the purpose of the oil added to the OF-glucose tubes?

3. Explain the difference between the indicators methyl red and phenol red. What color is each indicator at a pH of 7.0?

4. In the sugar fermentation tubes, explain the difference between two tubes that turned yellow but only one has an air bubble in the Durham tube.

5. Acetoin is a neutral end-product of fermentation. What tests could be used to determine if acetoin is present? Why?

6. Both Urease and gelatinase are enzymes that break down what macromolecule?

7. What would you expect to find in a hydrolyzed tube of gelatin? (hint: what is the end-product from gelatin breakdown?)

Endnote

1. Adapted from *Laboratory Exercises in Microbiology,* by Keith E. Belcher. Copyright © 2012 by Kendall Hunt Publishing Company. Reprinted by permission.

LAB 9

Microbial Metabolism Part 2

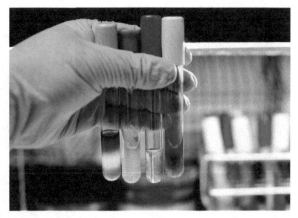

© Jarun Ontakrai/Shutterstock.com

In addition to the carbohydrate and protein biochemical assays from Part 1, microorganisms also possess many additional enzymes for oxidizing substrates, reducing substrates, carrying out anaerobic respiration, ⌐and deamination and decarboxylation of amino acids. All these pathways are vital to growth and cellular functions. In this lab, you will test several species of bacteria for their ability to, deaminate phenylalanine, produce hydrogen sulfide, decarboxylate ornithine, produce indole, reduce nitrate, produce oxidase, and produce catalase. A list of each mentioned assay can be seen in detail as follows.⌐[1]

Did you Know??

Most hospitals and labs use various versions of all the biochemical tests we have performed in LABS 8 and 9 and roll them up into one simple test called an **Enterotube**! These tubes provide a quick identification based on all the biochemical results, which point to the unknown microbe's genus and species.

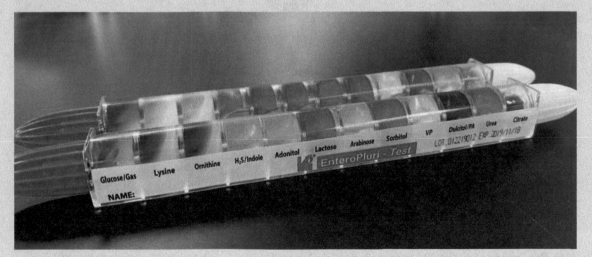

© Carolyn Caudle and Joshua Ohair

Phenylalanine Deamination

In the phenylalanine deamination assay in this image, a positive test stains green (right tube) when ferric chloride is added, and a negative test will appear yellow/brown (left tube).

© Carolyn Caudle and Joshua Ohair

⌐Members of the genus *Proteus* and *Providencia* produce the enzyme phenylalanine deaminase which removes the amino group from phenylalanine and forms a keto-acid (phenylpyruvate) and ammonia. Deamination of phenylalanine is tested for by the addition of ferric chloride which reacts with keto-acids to produce a green color.⌐[1]

Hydrogen Sulfide Production

In the assay for H$_2$S (hydrogen sulfide) production, a black precipitate will form indicating a positive test (top tube).

© Carolyn Caudle and Joshua Ohair

⌐In the hydrogen sulfide assay, organisms that can reduce sulfur to hydrogen sulfide will generate a black precipitate. This precipitate is formed when hydrogen sulfide combines with iron to form ferric sulfide.⌐[1] Many sulfur-reducing bacteria (SRB) belong to the phylum Firmicutes that include genus *Bacillus*. Hydrogen sulfide also is responsible for the "rotten egg" smell in soil.

Motility, Indole, Ornithine Decarboxylase (MIO)

MIO assays as shown in this picture look for motility, indole production (left tube positive, red color), and ornithine decarboxylase (both tubes positive, purple color)

© Carolyn Caudle and Joshua Ohair

In this single assay, three different characteristics are tested. The first, motility, is judged by the presence of growth throughout the semi-agar tube. ⌐Second, Indole testing, which looks for the ability of an organism to produce indole from tryptophan by the tryptophanase enzyme. In the addition of Kovac's reagent, tryptophan-containing media will turn red in the presence of indole. Then the third, decarboxylation of ornithine, tests for the ability of an organism to use the amino acid ornithine as a source of carbon. In this third part, removal of the amine will cause a pH rise. The pH-sensitive dye bromocresol purple will change in color from yellow to purple if ornithine decarboxylase is present.⌐[1]

Nitrate Reduction Test

The nitrate reduction test in this picture tests for an organism's ability to reduce nitrate. A red color is produced when reagents A and B (α-naphthylamine and sulfanilic acid) are added (tube far right) in response to nitrate reduction to nitrite. If nitrate is reduced to nitrogen gas, bubbles will be present in the Durham tube (tube far left) as well as a red color will be produced when zinc dust is added.

© Carolyn Caudle and Joshua Ohair

⌐The nitrate reduction test looks for an organism's ability to reduce nitrate to nitrite and/or nitrogen gas. The nitrogen cycle is very important in the fixation and assimilation of nitrogen-containing compounds in the soil (nitrogen nutrient cycle). To determine If nitrate was reduced to nitrite, reagents A and B (α-naphthylamine and sulfanilic acid) are added to the tube after incubation for 18–24 hours and will turn red if nitrite is present. To determine if nitrite was further reduced to nitrogen gas, bubbles will be present in the Durham tube as well as a red color will be produced when zinc dust is added.⌐[1]

Catalase Test

In the catalase test featured, bubbles will appear above colonies (right side of the plate) that are positive for catalase when hydrogen peroxide is added.

© Carolyn Caudle and Joshua Ohair

⌐Most aerobic organisms produce hydrogen peroxide during normal metabolism. Hydrogen peroxide is toxic to most cells and must be readily decomposed. Catalase is an enzyme that promotes the decomposition of hydrogen peroxide into water and oxygen.⌐[1]

Oxidase Test

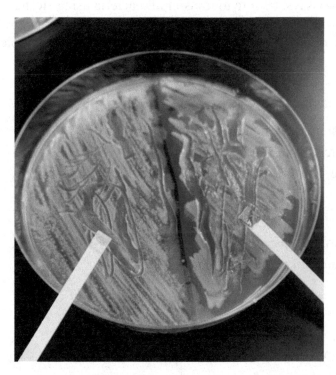

In this nutrient agar plate, two different species of bacteria *Pseudomonas* (right side) and *E. coli.* (left side) are tested for cytochrome oxidase. A positive test will turn the tip of the test strip purple (right)

© Carolyn Caudle and Joshua Ohair

⌐Many organisms transfer electrons to various cytochromes and ultimately to oxygen to form water. The last enzyme in the cytochrome system is cytochrome oxidase. The oxidase test is often used to identify members of the genera *Neisseria, Pseudomonas, Alcaligenes,* and *Aeromonas*. Organisms belonging to these genera turn oxidase test strips purple.⌐[1]

Exercise 9: Microbial Metabolism (Part II)

In part II of microbial metabolism, we will look at the several key biochemical assays used to identify bacterial strains based on genus and species. After this exercise, you will know the indicators used for each assay and what a positive or negative result implies.

Objective(s)

1. Know what a positive and negative result looks like for phenylalanine deamination, hydrogen sulfide production, decarboxylation of ornithine, indole production, reduction of nitrate, oxidase, and catalase assay.

2. Understand which enzymes are important in each assay performed.

3. Be able to identify certain bacteria based on their biochemical assay results.

Materials Needed

For the following tests/assays, be sure to transfer all bacteria using sterile techniques with the inoculating loop. For agar plates and slant tubes, you will gently scrape the bacteria to the surface of the media without breaking the agar. For deep tubes, you will pierce the agar with your inoculating loop.

Phenylalanine Deamination

1. Two phenylalanine slant tubes
2. Bacteria cultures: *E. coli* and *Proteus*
3. Ferric chloride

Hydrogen Sulfide Production

1. Two peptone iron deeps
2. Bacterial cultures: *E. coli* and *Proteus*

MIO

1. Two MIO deeps
2. Bacterial cultures: *Enterobacter* and *Proteus*
3. Kovacs reagent

Nitrate Reduction Test

1. Three test tubes of nitrate broth (Durham tubes inside)
2. Bacterial Cultures, *Bacillus, Lactococcus,* and *Pseudomonas*
3. Nitrate reagent A (alpha-naphthylamine)
4. Nitrate reagent B (sulfanilic acid)

Catalase Test

1. Tryptic soy agar plate
2. Bacteria cultures, *Lactococcus,* and *Bacillus*
3. Hydrogen peroxide

Oxidase Test

1. Tryptic soy agar plate
2. Bacteria cultures: *E. coli* and *Pseudomonas*
3. Oxidase test strips (2)

Enterotube

1. One Enterotube
2. One unknown pure culture

Procedure(s)

Read all procedures carefully. Keep note of procedures that will be carried out on Day 1 of your experiment and Day 2 (the following lab session). For results to LAB 9, bacteria must be incubated for at least 24 hours in order to observe growth.

Phenylalanine Deamination

DAY 1

1. Streak the slants heavily with the bacteria
2. Incubate the tubes for one to two days at 37°C

DAY 2

1. After incubation, (or next lab period) observe the growth. (pro tip: Growth will look like a clear film all over the agar of the slant tube)
2. Add four or five drops of ferric chloride reagent to the top of the slant
3. Look for a positive test which will result in a dark green color

Hydrogen Sulfide Production

DAY 1

1. Using your inoculating loop collect one loopful using the sterile technique from your broth cultures: *E. coli* and *Proteus.*
2. Stab the peptone iron deeps with the bacteria on the loop (*E coli.* into one tube and *Proteus* into the other tube)
3. Incubate for 24–48 hours at 37°C

DAY 2

1. Observe the growth and the black color that indicates a positive test
2. Record your results

MIO Test

DAY 1

1. Stab the MIO tubes with the bacterial cultures provided to you (*Enterobacter* and *Proteus*) with your inoculating loop into separate tubes.
2. Incubate the tubes for at least 24 hours in the incubator at 37°C

DAY 2

1. Compare the inoculated tubes and observe the growth
2. Motility is determined by a cloudy area diffusing from the line of the stab
3. Look for a positive ornithine decarboxylation reaction that will produce a purple color
4. Add 4 or 5 drops of Kovacs reagent, gently mix
5. Look for a positive indole test which will have a cherry red color

Nitrate Reduction Test

DAY 1

1. Label three nitrate tubes with the organisms which will be added (*Bacillus, Lactococcus, and Pseudomonas*)
2. Inoculate the three tubes with the above mentioned bacteria, separately into each tube, with your inoculating loop.
3. Incubate for 24–48 hours

DAY 2

1. Observe for growth
2. Add five drops of nitrate reagent A and five drops of reagent B into the tubes
3. Gently shake the tubes
4. You will see a red color if the nitrate is reduced to nitrite
5. Look for air bubbles in the Durham tubes to indicate that gas is produced.

Catalase

DAY 1

1. Divide the tryptic agar plate in half by drawing a line on the bottom of the plate with a sharpie
2. Streak one half of the plate with *Lactococcus* and the other half with *Bacillus*
3. Incubate for 24–48 h at 37°C in the incubator

DAY 2

1. Observe the growth on the plate and notice the different cultures on each side
2. Add 5–10 drops of hydrogen peroxide to each culture
3. A positive reaction will produce bubbles

Oxidase

DAY 1

1. Divide the tryptic agar plate in half by drawing a line on the bottom of the plate with a sharpie
2. Inoculate one half of the plate with *E. coli* and the other half with *Pseudomonas*
3. Incubate for 24 to 48 hours

DAY 2

1. Observe the growth on the plate and notice the different cultures on each side
2. Using an oxidase test strip, smear the top of the strip in one side of the plate
3. Repeat with a new test strip for the other side of the plate
4. Look for an oxidase-positive test strip which will turn a dark purple color

Enterotube

DAY 1

1. Grab one Enterotube Test for each group
   Note: There will be a long wire inside the tube, do not pull this out yet. . . . Follow the instructions as follows.
2. Remove both caps from the Enterotube.
3. The Blue end with the bent wire is the handle and the pointy side is where you will touch your bacteria. (Do not take the wire out)
4. Dip the end you removed the white cap from into the test tube labeled "unknown."
5. Pull the wire through the Enterotube so the tip goes through each compartment but do not take the wire all the way out.
6. Reinsert the wire by pushing it back through all the compartments.
7. Replace the caps (both blue and white) loosely
8. Using a toothpick poke or sterilized needle, poke a hole in the last eight compartments.
9. Put your name on it and place it on the incubator.

DAY 2

1. Observe each compartment for a color change and record the results.

Results

Phenylalanine Deamination and Hydrogen Sulfide Production

Organism	Growth (yes or no)	Phenylalanine Deamination (+ or -)	Hydrogen Sulfide Production (+ or -)
E. Coli			
Proteus			

MIO

Organism	Growth (yes or no)	Motility (yes or no)	Indole (+ or -)	Ornithine Decarboxylase (+ or -)
Proteus				
Enterobacter				

Nitrate Reduction Test

Organism	Color after adding Nitrate Reagents A and B	Color after adding Zinc (optional)	Gas production (+ or -)
Bacillus			
Lactococcus			
Pseudomonas			

Catalase Test

Organism	Bubbles present after adding Hydrogen Peroxide (yes or no)
Lactococcus	
Bacillus	

Oxidase Test

Organism	Color of Oxidase test strip
E. coli	
Pseudomonas	

Enterotube

Test Compartment in tube	Positive or Negative test
Glucose/Gas fermentation	
Lysine decarboxylation	
Ornithine decarboxylation	
Indole and Hydrogen sulfide production	
Adonitol fermentation	
Lactose fermentation	
Arabinose fermentation	
Sorbitol fermentation	
VP Acetoin production (Voges-Proskauer)	

Test Compartment in tube	Positive or Negative test
Dulcitol/PA-Dulcitol fermentation and phenylalanine deamination	
Urea hydrolysis	
Citrate utilization	

EnteroPluri-Test Reference Bacterial Strains

Microorganisms	Glucose	Gas	Lysine	Ornithine	H₂S	Indole	Adonitol	Lactose	Arabinose	Sorbitol	VP	Dulcitol	PA	Urea	Citrate	Acceptable biocodes
Escherichia coli ATCC 25922	+	±	+	+	-	+	-	+	+	+	-	-	-	-	-	75340
Proteus mirabilis ATCC 25933	+	±	-	+	+	-	-	-	-	-	±	-	+	+	±	66007
Klebsiella pneumoniae ATCC 13883	+	±	+	-	-	-	+	+	+	+	±	+	-	±	+	70773-70771 70753-70751
Salmonella typhimurium ATCC 14028	+	±	+	±	+	-	-	-	+	+	-	-	-	-	±	52140
Pseudomonas aeruginosa * ATCC 27853	-	-	-	-	-	-	-	-	±	-	-	-	-	±	+	*

Questions

1. Catalase is an enzyme that converts hydrogen peroxide (H_2O_2) into water (H_2O) and oxygen (O_2). Write the chemical equation below for this reaction.

2. Following is an image of phenylalanine, explain what phenylalanine deaminase does to this substrate? What does a positive test for phenylalanine deaminase look like?

Phenylalanine

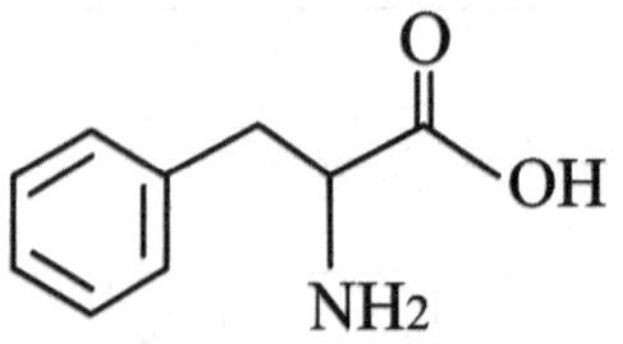

© Timonina/Shutterstock.com

3. Based on the results from your Enterotube and using the reference chart provided, what microorganism was your unknown? Is there a possibility it could be a different genus or species than the reference?

4. In the following reaction, name the compound that is reduced. What test is performed to confirm this? What does a positive test look like?

$$2\,NO_3^- + 12\,H^+ \rightarrow N_2 + 6\,H_2O$$

5. Why does hydrogen peroxide bubble when poured onto a cut on your skin?

6. Why does the black precipitant from hydrogen sulfide production show up toward the bottom of the tube?

7. What other ways can microorganisms be identified besides using biochemical testing?

Endnote

1. Adapted from *Laboratory Exercises in Microbiology,* by Keith E. Belcher. Copyright © 2012 by Kendall Hunt Publishing Company. Reprinted by permission.

LAB 10

Serial Dilutions and Plating Methods

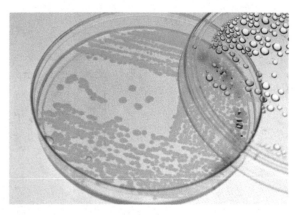

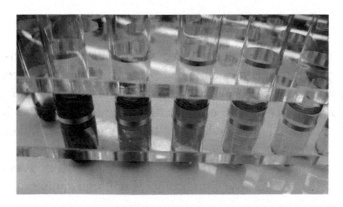

Serial dilution for direct counting

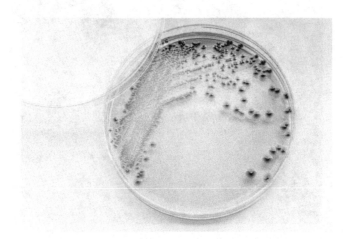

Plating methods for colony isolation)

Serial Dilutions

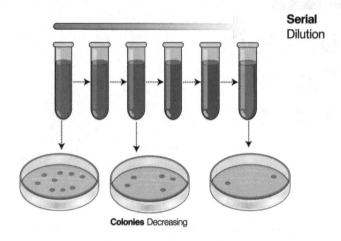

Serial
Dilution

Colonies Decreasing

© Art of Science/shutterstock.com

To obtain a total cell count, viable or standard colony counting methods must be employed to determine the number of living cells in a sample. To determine the **viable count**, we carry out the **spread plate technique**. To do this, a culture is diluted and measured aliquots are spread onto an appropriate agar medium. ⌐ After incubation, the colonies are counted and the original number of viable cells is calculated based on knowledge of the dilutions used. Although it is generally assumed that on plates containing 30 to 300 isolated colonies, each colony grew from a single cell, many microbiologists prefer to report the results of a viable count as **colony-forming units** (CFU)/mL rather than cells/mL, because some colonies will inevitably arise from unbroken clumps and aggregations.

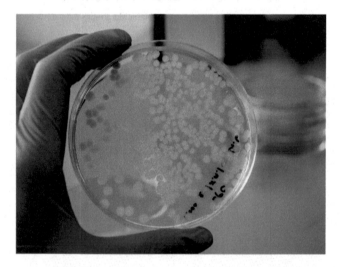

Each white circle in this photo is one colony

© MyFavoriteTime/Shutterstock.com

Viable counts can be used to monitor the growth of an organism in laboratory culture or to follow the progress of an industrial microbiological process. Colony counts are also used to grade milk and to test foodstuff for pathogens or spoilage organisms since only living cells cause damage. ⌐[1]

How to Write a Dilution?

⌐ Example 1: If 1.0 mL of sample is mixed with 9.0 mL of diluent, the dilution is 1/ 1 + 9 or 1/10. This dilution is read one to ten because one volume is diluted to a total of ten volumes. Dilutions are written in several ways. A 1/10 dilution can also be given as 1:10, and because 1/10 is 0.1, the dilution can be expressed as the exponential number, 10^{-1}. Thus a 1/100 dilution is also a 10^{-2} dilutions, $1/1000 = 10^{-3}$, and so on. ⌐[2]

Try it . . . . Write out all the ways a 10 mL sample mixed with 990 mL of diluent can be expressed.

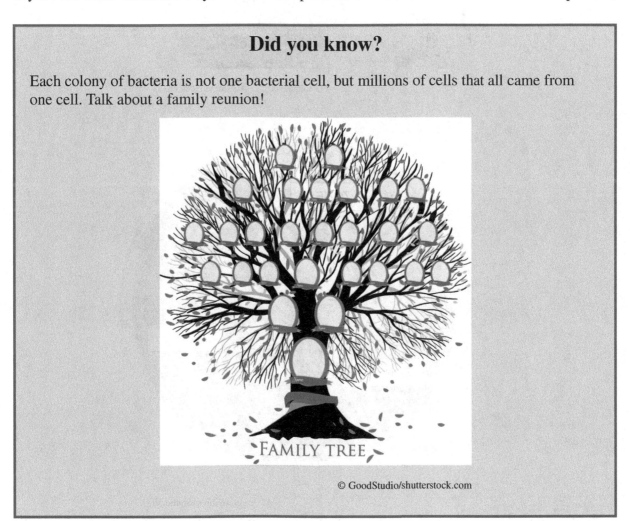

Did you know?

Each colony of bacteria is not one bacterial cell, but millions of cells that all came from one cell. Talk about a family reunion!

FAMILY TREE

© GoodStudio/shutterstock.com

Plating Methods

⌐ In order to separate and grow microorganisms in **pure culture**, many types of media need to be tried. A pure culture consists of a single species of a microorganism growing isolated from any other organism. Several methods are available to sort out the individual members of a mixed microbial population.

Most commonly, the individual cells are physically separated on an agar plate. Each separate cell will then give rise to an isolated colony upon incubation. In this exercise, the **streak-plate method** will be employed to obtain a pure culture. An inoculating loop is used to draw the inoculum back and forth across an agar plate to separate the individual cells of a microbial population. ⌐[1]

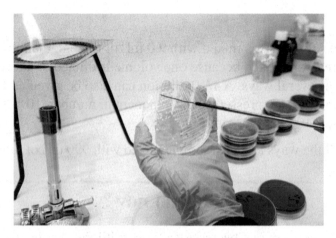

© Mohammed_Al_Ali/shutterstock.com

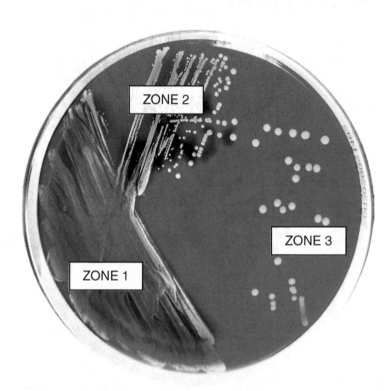

© eczserapyilmaz/Shutterstock.com

This picture displays a typical steak plate, which contains threedistinct zones. Zone 1 is created by transferring 1–2 loopful of culture to the clean media plate and gently spreading with an inoculating loop in one corner of the agar plate. Zones 2 and 3 are created by repeating this step and flaming the inoculating loop after each subsequent zone is streaked. In this way, fewer and fewer bacteria remain on the inoculating loop and in each zone. This process helps spread out bacteria on the agar plate and create individual colonies. Zone 3 will most likely be the only zone with colonies depending on the CFU/mL in the original culture suspension.

Exercise 10: Serial Dilution and Streak Plating

In this lab, you will be performing two different experiments. In part 1, you will dilute a suspension of bacteria to determine the CFU/mL by direct counting. In part 2, you will learn how to isolate individual colonies through the streak-plate method.

Objective(s)

1. To learn how to calculate CFU/mL by using the serial dilution methodology.
2. To properly isolate colonies from a mixed culture by employing the streak-plate isolation technique.
3. To know what a viable cell and a pure colony are.

Materials Needed

Part 1 Serial Dilutions

1. One culture tube of broth media containing *E. coli*
2. Six tubes with 9.0 mL sterile water
3. Sterile 1 mL pipettes
4. Spreader (either glass or plastic disposable)
5. Three sterilized nutrient agar plates
6. 75% Ethanol solution (if using glass spreader)
7. Bunsen burner

Part 2 Streak Plating

1. One mixed culture tube of broth media containing *Staph, Pseudomonas,* and *Escherichia*
2. Inoculating loop
3. One nutrient agar plate
4. Bunsen burner

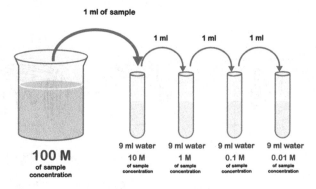

Science Experiment ● ● ●

SERIAL DILUTION

© BigBearCamera/shutterstock.com

Procedure

Part 1 Serial Dilutions

Day 1

1. Label six tubes containing 9.0 mL sterile water, 10^{-1}, 10^{-2}, 10^{-3}, 10^{-4}, 10^{-5}, 10^{-6}
2. Label three nutrient agar plates 10^{-4}, 10^{-5}, 10^{-6}
3. Gently mix the culture tube provided by swirling to evenly distribute the cells in the broth media suspension.
4. Aseptically remove 1.0 mL of the stock culture using a 1.0 mL sterile pipette. Pipet the 1 mL of cells into the 10^{-1} dilution blank (the first dilution tube).
5. Discard the pipette into the container on the lab bench.
6. Gently mix the 10^{-1} dilution tube by swirling to resuspend the cells.
7. With a fresh 1.0 mL sterile pipette remove 1.0 mL from the 10^{-1} tube and transfer it to the 10^{-2} (second dilution tube) and gently swirl to mix.
8. Changing the pipette between tubes, continue the serial tenfold dilutions till you complete transfers with all tubes.
9. With a new sterile pipette, transfer 1 mL from dilution tube 10^{-4} to the corresponding nutrient agar plate which is labeled 10^{-4}
10. Spread the inoculated plate using the spreader provided so that the culture is spread evenly on top of the agar plate. If using a glass spreader, dip into the alcohol, then briefly place the spreader into the Bunsen flame just long enough to ignite the alcohol. (pro tip: Be careful not to drip the burning alcohol on yourself or others! Do NOT keep the spreader in the flame too long, just long enough to catch on fire)
11. When all the plates have been inoculated, invert them and incubate them for 24 hours at 37°C. ⌐[1]

Day 2

1. Retrieve plates from incubator 37°C, unless it has been more than 24 hours plates will be in 4°C.
2. Choose the plates with 30 to 300 colonies for counting.
3. Record your data in the Results section and perform the required calculations.

Part 2 Streak Plating

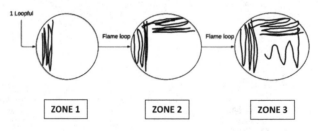

© Carolyn Caudle and Joshua Ohair

Day 1

1. ⌐ Each student will prepare a streak plate of the mixed culture.
2. Label the bottom of your agar plate with your name and lab section number.
3. Using sterile technique flame the inoculating loop. Allow the loop to cool for a moment.
4. Shake the liquid culture of bacteria by gently tapping the tube.
5. Open the culture tube by removing the cap with your fourth and fifth fingers of the hand holding the loop. Flame the mouth of the tube.
6. Insert the loop and place the loop into the liquid. Remove a loopful of culture.
7. Flame the mouth of the tube and replace the cap.
8. Carefully, so as not to lose any of the cultures, lift the lid of your petri dish and touch the loop to the agar. Gently move the loop back and forth across the agar. (STAY IN ZONE 1)
9. Remove the loop and close the lid onto the plate.
10. Flame the loop again.
11. Turn the plate a quarter turn and touch the loop to the edge of the agar near where you want to continue streaking the cells.
12. Touch the cooling loop to the previous streak and drag the loop through those cells. Only drag your loop through once or twice and then continue moving the loop back and forth (STAY IN ZONE 2) ⌐[1]
13. Repeat steps 10–12 one more time to create zone 3. When streaking zone 3, barely touch the tip of the inoculating loop to the agar surface.
14. Incubate the plate inverted overnight at 30°C

Day 2

1. Retrieve plates from incubator 37°C, unless it has been more than 24 hours plates will be at 4°C.
2. Observe colonies and record results.

Results

Part 1 Serial Dilution

Plate Dilution	Is the number of CFUs between 30 and 300?	Number of CFUs on plate	The appearance of colonies on the plate
10^{-4}			
10^{-5}			
10^{-6}			

Colony-forming units per ml (CFUs/mL) in original sample: _____

(This is calculated by multiplying the number of colonies times the dilution factor. The dilution factor is the inverse of the plate dilution. For example, the 10^{-3} plate dilution is the dilution factor 10^3)

Part 2 Streak-Plate Method

Draw observation of plate

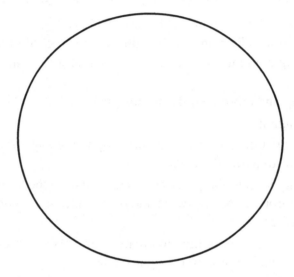

© Carolyn Caudle and Joshua Ohair

Colony Morphology and Identification

Colonies	*Staphylococcus*	*Pseudomonas*	*Escherichia*	**Other**(s)
Size				
Color				
Elevation				

Questions

1. How did you figure out which colony was on the mixed plate?

2. What would you conclude if an inoculated plate had colonies between the streak lines?

3. If your streak plate had no single colonies, what might be the issue? How could you fix the problem?

4. From your serial dilutions, which dilution tube(s) contained 30–300 colonies when spread out on a growth agar plate? Which dilution tube(s) had too many colonies to count and why?

5. What other ways can bacterial concentrations be determined? Which is more accurate, direct or indirect methods? Explain.

6. Determine the number of bacteria present in CFU/mL from the following information.
Dilution tube used to count cell: third tube
Number of cells counted: 165
Volume transferred in each dilution: 1 mL
The volume of each dilution tube: 99 mL

Endnotes

1. Adapted from *Techniques of Microbiology: A Laboratory Manual*, by Deborah A. Polayes. Copyright © 2021 by Kendall Hunt Publishing Company. Reprinted by permission.
2. Adapted from *Laboratory Exercises in Microbiology*, by Keith E. Belcher. Copyright © 2012 by Kendall Hunt Publishing Company. Reprinted by permission.

LAB 11

Biotechnology for Isolating Microbial DNA

© luchschenF/shutterstock.com

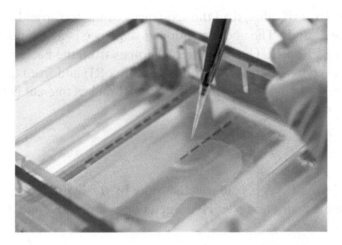

© SatawatK/shutterstock.com

In this lab, you will perform a **restriction enzyme digest** and visualize the results with **gel electrophoresis**.

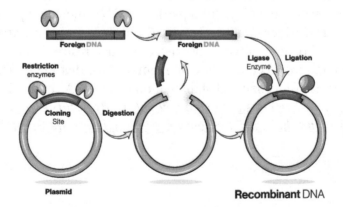

Restriction enzymes are used in biotechnology to create recombinant DNA through the cutting of specific sequences in both the foreign DNA and the vector DNA

© Art of Science/Shutterstock.com

Restriction Enzymes

⌐ Restriction enzymes are proteins produced by bacteria to prevent or restrict invasion by foreign DNA (e.g., bacterial viruses). Restriction enzymes cut the foreign DNA into pieces so that it cannot function. Restriction enzymes recognize and cut at specific places along the DNA molecule, called restriction sites. There are many different types of restriction enzymes made by many different bacteria. Each restriction enzyme cuts at a specific nucleotide sequence that is usually unique to that enzyme. Often, a restriction site is a four- or six-base-pair (bp) sequence that is a palindrome. A **DNA palindrome** is a sequence in which the "top" strand read from 5' to 3' is the same as the "bottom" strand read from 5' to 3'. For example,

5' GAATTC 3'

3' CTTAAG 5'

is a DNA palindrome. To verify this, read the sequences of the top strand and the bottom strand from the 5' ends to the 3' ends. The abovementioned sequence is also a restriction site for the restriction enzyme called **EcoRI**. The name EcoRI comes from the bacterium in which the enzyme was first discovered—Escherichia coli RY 13 (EcoRI) and from the fact that it was the first restriction enzyme (I) found in this organism. EcoRI makes one cut between the G and the A in each of the DNA strands.

5' G|AATTC 3'

3' CTTAA|G 5'

After the cuts are made, the DNA is held together only by the hydrogen bonds between the four bases in the middle of the restriction site. Hydrogen bonds are weak, and the two DNA strands separate.

Cut DNA: 5' G_ _ _AATTC 3'

3' CTTAA _ _ _G 5' ⌐

As you can see, when EcoRI cuts a DNA molecule it leaves single-stranded "tails" on the new ends. This type of end is called a "**sticky end**" because it is easy to rejoin it to a complementary sticky end. ⌐ A restriction enzyme digest of a particular DNA molecule produces a distinctive pattern of DNA fragments, which can then be visualized through gel electrophoresis. The characteristic number and pattern of bands produced by each restriction enzyme cutting a specific piece of DNA are, in effect, a "**DNA fingerprint**" for that DNA. The banding patterns are made visible by the use of a chemical stain that binds to DNA. In this lab, the DNA will be stained by GelGreen. ⌐ *The DNA molecule you will study in this experiment is the lambda bacteriophage genome, and the restriction enzymes you will use are BamHI, EcoRI, and HindIII.*

Lambda Bacteriophage DNA

Structure of bacteriophage

Capsid head

Nucleic acid (DNA)

Collar

Sheath

Baseplate

Spikes

Tail fiber

© Designua/shutterstock.com

Lambda is a bacteriophage, a virus that infects only bacteria. Specifically, lambda infects *E. coli* bacteria. Lambda has a relatively small double-stranded DNA genome (48,502 base pairs long). The relative simplicity of the organism and the fact that it grows in bacteria and is easy to produce in the lab makes it perfect for this restriction enzyme cutting in this experiment.

How to use a Micropipettor

© SatawatK/shutterstock.com

Micropipettes are not limited to a set volume but can be adjusted to any volume within the range of the pipette. The maximum volume that can be pipetted is indicated on the plunger button. In the lab, we have P1000, P200, and P20 pipettors, with their useful range being 200–1000 μL, 20–200 μL, and 2–20 μL, respectively. Always use the smallest size pipettor that is able to handle the volume you want to pipette. This will lead to the greatest accuracy in your measurement. For example, if you wanted to pipet 200 μL, it is better to use the P200 rather than the P1000.

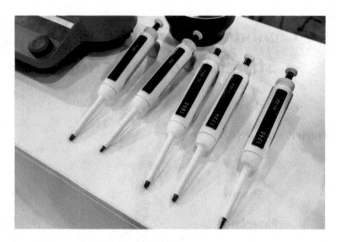

© FOTOGRIN/shutterstock.com

On the front of the pipettor, there is a window containing three numbers. These numbers specify the volume that will be pipetted. The volume is read from top to bottom. The numbers are either red or black. To adjust the volume, hold the pipette in one hand and turn the adjustment knob that is just above the volume window. Do NOT adjust the volume above the maximum for a given pipette. Anything above the maximum value will put the pipette out of calibration.

To use the pipettor, a tip needs to be attached. Hold the pipette and press down on the tip to attach it to the shaft. Press the plunger to the first stop (This is the load volume.). With the plunger at the first stop, put the tip into the liquid. Slowly release the plunger to draw up the liquid. Always make sure the tip is below the liquid so that no air bubbles get into the tip. Never allow the

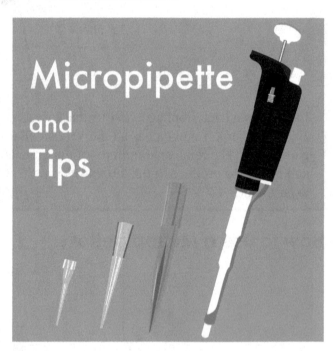

© 1.609kkm/shutterstock.com

plunger to snap back into position by removing your finger too quickly. To dispense the liquid, touch the tip against the sidewall of the tube, press the plunger to the first stop to expel the liquid, and then press the plunger to the second stop to expel any remaining fluid.

How to Run a DNA gel

⌐ **Gel electrophoresis** is a widely used technique for separating charged molecules such as DNA, RNA, and proteins through the use of electricity. Electrophoresis is frequently performed using an agarose gel like the one you will use in this lab. Agarose is a polysaccharide like agar or pectin. The gel is formed by dissolving the agarose

© luchschenF/shutterstock.com

in a boiling buffer, pouring the resulting agarose solution into a gel mold, and allowing the agarose solution to cool. As the agarose solution cools and solidifies, it forms a gel matrix. The molecules to be separated are moved through the slab of gelled agarose by applying a voltage across the gel. When the gel is running, the "red" electrode of the electrophoresis chamber is positively charged and the "black" electrode is negatively charged. A negatively charged molecule (such as DNA) migrates through the gel toward the positive electrode.

GEL ELECTROPHORESIS APPARATUS

migrated samples on the gel   gel under UV light   photo of the gel

© M. PATTHAWEE/Shutterstock.com

Linear fragments of DNA like the ones you will work with in this lab move through the gel according to their length and thus separate out by size. *Shorter fragments move more quickly than longer fragments, and the fragments of differing sizes become concentrated into separate bands.*

Exercise 11: Biotechnology for Isolating Microbial DNA

In today's lab, you will see first-hand how restriction enzymes work and how DNA fragments can be visualized by gel electrophoresis. This lab displays one methodology of biotechnology and how scientists have converted a natural bacterial defense into a system for constructing recombinant DNA with implementations for genetic cloning.

Objective(s)

1. How an understanding of restriction enzymes allows us to analyze and manipulate DNA in the laboratory.
2. To properly carryout skills related to micropipetting and DNA gel electrophoresis.
3. Understanding how biotechnology can impact the world we live in.

Materials Needed

1. Tube of lambda DNA
2. Dehydrated EcoRI restriction enzyme (pink tube)
3. Dehydrated BamHI restriction enzyme (blue tube)
4. Dehydrated HindIII restriction enzyme (green tube)
5. Empty yellow tube with cap
6. Tube of 10× loading dye (15 µL)
7. Micropipette tips and micropipettes (for measuring 2–22 µL)
8. Microcentrifuge tube rack
9. Gel electrophoresis chamber
10. 0.8% agarose solution
11. 1× tris–acetate–EDTA (TAE) electrophoresis buffer
12. water bath or incubator at 37°C
13. GelGreen stain
14. DNA ladder

Procedure

⌐ *DAY 1*

Set Up the Restriction Digests

1. Add 20 µL of lambda DNA to one of the tubes containing dehydrated enzyme. Resuspend and mix the dried enzyme with the DNA by pipetting the DNA up and down a few times until the dye contained within the restriction enzyme/ buffer mixture is evenly dispersed throughout the reaction. There should be no concentration of the blue color in the tube if the DNA and enzymes are mixed sufficiently.
2. Close the tube with its matching-colored cap and place it upright in the microcentrifuge tube rack provided.
3. Repeat steps 1 and 2 for each of the two additional tubes containing enzyme and for the yellow control tube. To prevent cross-contamination between the tubes, use a fresh pipet tip for each tube. Remember, there is no enzyme in the control tube, so there will be no dye to disperse in the yellow control tube.
4. Incubate all reaction tubes for a minimum of 20 minutes at 37°C. Your instructor may have you incubate the reactions for a longer period.

DAY 2

Casting Agarose Gel

1. Seal the ends of the gel-casting tray with masking tape or other equipment suitable for your gel apparatus and insert the well-forming comb.
2. Place the gel-casting tray out of the way on the lab bench, so that the agarose poured in the next step can solidify undisturbed.
3. Carefully pour enough agarose solution into the casting tray to fill it to a depth of about 6 to 7 mm. The gel should cover only about one-half the height of the comb teeth.

4. The gel will become cloudy as it solidifies (15–20 min). Do not move or jar the casting tray while the agarose is solidifying.

5. When the agarose has solidified, unseal the ends of the casting tray. Place the tray in the gel electrophoresis chamber, so that the comb is closest to the negative (black) electrode.

6. Fill the box with 1× TAE buffer, to a level that just covers the entire surface of the gel.

7. Gently remove the comb, being careful not to rip the wells.

8. Make certain that sample wells left by the comb are completely submerged. If there are "dimples" around the wells, slowly add buffer until they disappear.

9. The gel is now ready to load with DNA.

Loading the Gel

1. Add 2 μL of loading dye to each reaction tube (including the control tube). Mix the dye with the DNA by pipetting up and down several times.

2. Add 2 μL of loading dye to 10 μL of DNA ladder in a separate micropipette tube.

3. Using a micropipette and following the given instructions, load each reaction and the control reaction into a separate well in the gel. You will use a total of *five wells (includes one DNA ladder lane, one control lane, and three digestion lanes).* Record the order in which you load the reactions. Load the entire volume of each reaction into each well. Use a fresh tip for each reaction tube.

4. To load each sample:

   a. Draw the sample to be loaded into the pipette tip.

   b. Steady the pipet over the well using two hands. Many find it useful to place their elbows on the lab bench to steady their hands as they load the gel.

   c. Fully expel any air at the end of the micropipette tip before loading the gel.
   (pro tip: If an air bubble forms a cap over a well, the DNA and loading dye will flow into the buffer around the edges of the well. Air bubbles pipetted into a well beneath the sample can distort how the sample runs. A bubble that pops or becomes dislodged and floats up through the sample can eject some of the samples from the well.)

   d. Dip the pipette tip through the surface of the buffer and position it just over the wall. (pro tip: Some people find it easier to gently rest the pipet tip on the edge of the well with the end of the tip just over the well.)

   e. Slowly expel the mixture. Sucrose in the loading dye weighs down the sample, causing it to sink to the bottom of the well. Note: Be careful not to punch the tip of the pipette through the bottom of the gel.

Electrophoresis of the Digest and Staining the Gel

1. Close the top of the electrophoresis chamber and connect the electrical leads to the power supply, anode to anode (red to red), and cathode to cathode (black to black). Make sure both electrodes are connected to the same channel of the power supply.

2. Turn the power supply on and set the voltage as directed by your instructor. Shortly after the voltage is applied, the loading dye should move through the gel toward the positive electrode of the electrophoresis apparatus.

3. The bromophenol blue in the loading dye migrates through the gel at the same rate as a DNA fragment approximately 300 base pairs long. Run the gel until the bromophenol blue is approximately 1 cm from the end of the gel.

4. Once the gel has run for a sufficient amount of time, turn off the power supply, disconnect the leads, and remove the top of the electrophoresis chamber.

5. Carefully remove the casting tray with the gel and slide the gel into the staining tray.

6. Measure the distance that the bromophenol blue dye front has traveled (in centimeters) through the gel by measuring the distance from the edge of the well closest to the bromophenol blue to the edge of the bromophenol blue band furthest from the wells (the band called the "dye front"). Record the data in the following space. If you will be doing your analysis of the gels from a photograph, make a small notch or another mark on the side of the gel to mark the location of the dye front. Mark the side of the dye front furthest from the wells. Make sure that the mark will be visible in a photograph.

    Distance migrated by dye front: _____.

7. Stain the gel according to the instructions provided by your instructor.

DAY 3

1. Observe gel and DNA fragments that have migrated through the agarose during your electrophoresis.

2. Measure the distance the DNA bands had traveled and record.

3. Calculate the size of the fragments ⌙

Results

Examine your stained gel on a transilluminator depending upon the stain you used. Your instructor may instead have you photograph the gel and perform your analysis using the photograph. Use the DNA ladder in lane 5 to calculate band sizes.

Bands observed (top to bottom)	Restriction Enzyme			Control	DNA ladder
	HindIII	EcoRI	BamHI	Lane 4	Lane 5
Band 1 size					
Band 2 size					
Band 3 size					
Band 4 size					
Band 5 size					
Band 6 size					
Band 7 size					
Band 8 size					
Band 9 size					
Band 10 size					
Band 11 size					
Band 12 size					

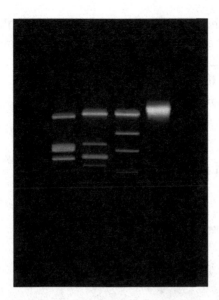

This is how your gel should look at the end after staining. (from left to right) Lane 1 is BamHI, Lane 2 is EcoRI, and Lane 3 is HindIII. The last lane with one band is your control.

Questions

1. ⌐ Why were the restriction enzyme digests done at 37°C?

2. Based on your results how many DNA fragments were produced by restriction enzyme digest with HindIII? EcoRI? BamHI?

3. Why does the control lane only have one band? What is it?

4. In gel electrophoresis, the DNA is placed inside wells at the top of the gel. The top of the gel is placed near the negative electrode and the current moves DNA toward the positive electrode. Why does this happen? What would happen if it was reversed, and the top of the gel was placed near the positive electrode?

    Use the following diagram to help explain your answers.

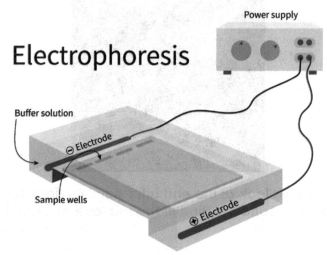

© M. PATTHAWEE/Shutterstock.com

5. You have a piece of DNA with the sequence shown below:

    5'-AAAGTCGCTGGAATTCACTGCATCCCCGG
    GGCTATATATGAATTCGATGCGTACTTGGCACG-3'

    3'-TTTCAGCGACCTTAAGTGACGTAGGGGCCCCGA
    TATATACTTAAGCTACGCATGAACCGTGC-5'

    You cut this fragment with the restriction enzyme EcoRI. The recognition site for EcoRI is shown as follows:

    5' GAATTC 3'

    3' CTTAAG 5'

    Below, show the fragments that would result from the restriction digest of that piece of DNA by EcoRI. Show all the base pairs and the overhanging ends of the fragments.

Endnote

1. Bracketed text throughout Lab 11: © Carolina Biological Supply Company. Reprinted by permission.

LAB 12

ELISA Immunoassay and The Antibody–Antigen Reaction

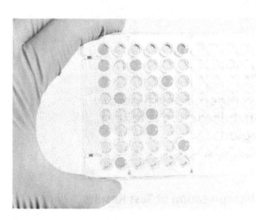

96-well plate ELISA

© Jarun Ontakrai/Shutterstock.com

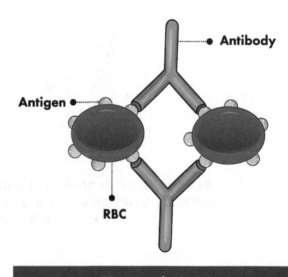

Hemagglutination

Blood typing antigen-antibody reaction

© Art of Science/Shutterstock.com

In this lab, you will investigate the antigen–antibody reaction. As seen in the following image, a basic IgG antibody, each antigen will only bind to a specific region on the antibody called the **epitope**. This binding is based on unique amino acid sequences that produce hydrophobic interactions, electrostatic, and Van der Waals forces between the antigen and variable region of the antibody.

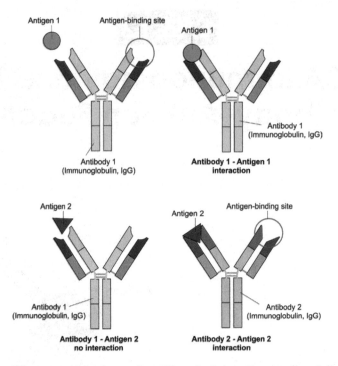

Recognition mechanism of antibody to antigen. Each type of antibody binds only to a specific antigen. Interaction is taking place in the epitope region

© Soleil Nordic/Shutterstock.com

Many labs across the country use this basic principle to test for diseases and antigens present in serum. One of the most common antigen–antibody tests is called as enzyme-linked immunosorbent assay (**ELISA**). ELISAs are currently used for food allergy testing, drug screenings, pregnancy tests, endotoxins from *E. coli*, HIV antibodies, SARS-CoV-2 antibodies, and antibodies from *Mycobacterium tuberculosis* to name a few. ELISA assays are generally carried out in 96-well plates (seen at top of page), allowing for multiple samples to be measured in a single experiment. However, one-time use strips are a preferred method in "rapid testing" and these ELISAs are called lateral flow immunoassays (see the following image).

Interpretation of Test Results

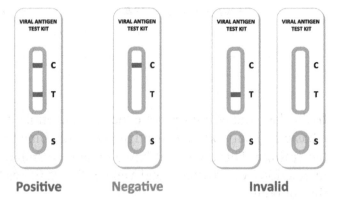

Interpretation of test results of the antigen test kit, lateral flow immunoassay for the qualitative detection of antigens such as hCG (pregnancy test) or SARS-CoV-2 viral antigens

© M. PATTHAWEE/Shutterstock.com

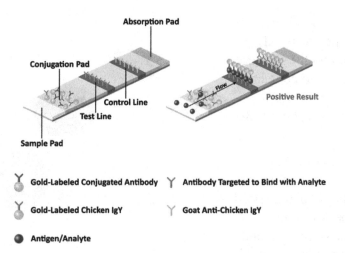

The basis of rapid antigen test kits with lateral flow immunoassay for the qualitative detection

© M. PATTHAWEE/Shutterstock.com

ELISAs measure antibodies, antigens, proteins, or glycoproteins using a capture antibody/antigen that is fixed to the testing strip or 96-well plate. If the target antigen/antibody is present, it will bind to the capture antibody/antigen and produce a chromogenic or color change visible to the naked eye. The three types of ELISAs are direct, indirect, and a sandwich (seen in the following diagram) and all rely on the same specific binding properties of antigen–antibody interactions.

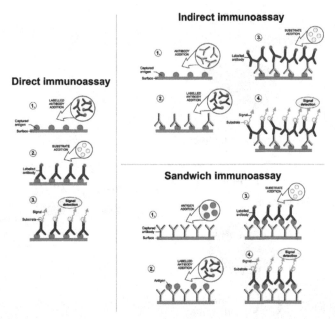

An immunoassay is used to measure the concentration of the antigen. The basic components of the test are antigen, labeled antibody, and substrate. Types of ELISAs are direct, indirect, and sandwich

© Soleil Nordic/Shutterstock.com

The antigen–antibody reaction is also used to test for blood types A, B, AB, and O. When the antigen on the surface of a red blood cell comes into contact with a corresponding antibody, a clumping of red blood cells occurs called **hemagglutination**.

In blood type testing, clumping is a positive test and confirms the antigens present on the blood sample being tested. For example, blood type A has the A-antigen on the surface of the cell and anti-B antibodies are found in serum. If a person with type A was given blood type B blood, the antigen-B antibodies would attack these red blood cells and cause clumping and potential death if not immediately reversed.

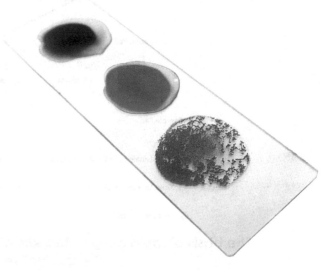

Hemagglutination of red blood cells. The blood sample on the far right is a positive hemagglutination reaction

© PHATCHARADA DUEANDAO/Shutterstock.com

ABO blood group

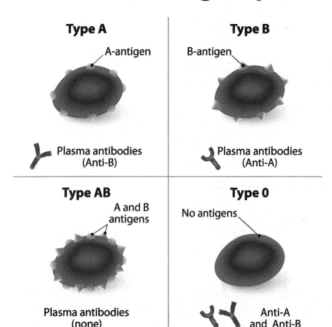

Type A
A-antigen
Plasma antibodies (Anti-B)

Type B
B-antigen
Plasma antibodies (Anti-A)

Type AB
A and B antigens
Plasma antibodies (none)

Type 0
No antigens
Anti-A and Anti-B

ABO Blood groups. There are four basic blood types, made up from combinations of type A and type B antigens

© Designua/Shutterstock.com

Blood gr. AB

Agglutination of blood type AB will occur when tested with both anti-B and anti-A antibodies

© Chamaiporn Naprom/Shutterstock.com

The Rh Factor⁺

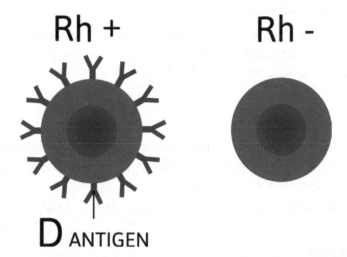

**Blood cells with antigen D (also known as Rh factor) and cells without it.
Blood cells with antigen D on the surface are Rh+**

© Betty Ray/Shutterstock.com

A second antigen on red blood cells known as antigen D is responsible for hemolytic disease of newborns. Mothers that are Rh- are at risk of their own body's immune system attacking their fetus, if the fetus is Rh +.

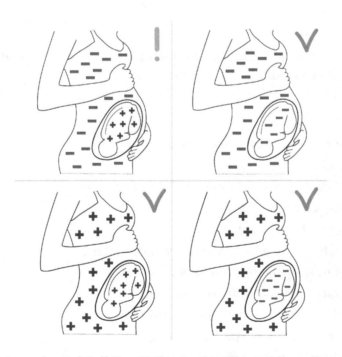

The newborn is at risk if the Rh factor is different than the mothers

© Betty Ray/Shutterstock.com

Exercise 12: ELISA Immunoassay and Blood Typing Antigen-Antibody Reaction

In today's lab, you will learn the importance of Immunoassays and how antigen–antibody reactions are involved in rapid testing. You will also perform a blood typing agglutination assay on your own blood sample to discover your blood type!

Objective(s)

1. To use an ELISA-based assay to learn how the antigen-antibody reaction works.
2. To understand through blood typing the hemagglutination reaction and the reasoning behind blood groups and the Rh factor.
3. To know how the antigen–antibody can be used in medical diagnosis and rapid testing.

Materials Needed

1. One ELISA test kit (includes supplies)
2. Two glass slides
3. Sterile lancet
4. Alcohol wipes
5. Anti-A antiserum, Anti-B antiserum, and Anti-D antiserum
6. Toothpicks

Procedure

Part I ELISA

1. Follow instruction manual provided by instructor: *AIDS Kit I: Simulation of HIV Detection by ELISA* or similar ELISA kit

Part II Blood Typing

1. With a wax pencil on a clean glass slide draw two circles.
2. Label one A and one B.
3. On a second slide draw a circle and label it as D.
4. Disinfect the finger with an alcohol wipe.
5. Prick the finger with a sterile lancet.
6. Place a drop of blood on each circle (three drops total).
7. Use a bandage to wrap the pricked finger.
8. On circle A, place a drop of Anti-A antiserum.
9. On circle B, place a drop of Anti-B antiserum.
10. On Circle D, place a drop of Anti-D antiserum.
11. Mix with a toothpick (use a different toothpick for each one).
12. Discard in the round red receptacles.
13. Record results.

Results

Part I ELISA

Test sample	Antigen detected (+ or -)	Control line detected (+ or -)

Part II Blood type

	Agglutination occurred (+ or -)	Antigens present on red blood cells (A, B, or none)
Agglutination with anti-A antiserum		
Agglutination with anti-B antiserum		
Agglutination with Rh factor		

Personal blood type based on agglutination: _____

Questions

1. Explain how ELISAs work and how a color change is detected in a positive test?

2. Which test samples from Part I had the antigen present? How did you know?

3. If a control line is not detected can the results of the test be trusted? Explain.

4. Explain what a positive blood typing test of a patient with A+ blood looks like if Anti-A antiserum, Anti-B antiserum, and Anti-D antiserum are each added individually to a drop of blood.

5. How can a father (blood type A) and a mother (blood type B) have an offspring with blood type O? Use a Punnett square to explain.

6. What makes the antigen–antibody reaction highly specific?

LAB 13

Antimicrobial Compounds and Antibiotic Sensitivity

© Jarun Ontakrai/shutterstock.com

Antimicrobial Agents

⌐ To disinfect is to kill or prevent the growth of vegetative microbial cells. Since disinfection does not necessarily destroy endospores or viruses, a disinfected object should not be considered sterile. Usually, a **disinfectant** is a chemical substance used on inanimate objects to lower the number of microbial populations. Only through **sterilization** can all microbial life be removed or destroyed. One of the most common sterilization techniques is through the use of an **autoclave**. This device uses high-pressure steam at 121°C to not only kill all microorganisms but spores as well. ⌐[1]

Oregano oil can be used as a disinfectant as it contains carvacrol and thymol, two antibacterial and antifungal compounds

© Madeleine Steinbach/Shutterstock.com

75% Alcohol is a common sanitizer that lowers microbial counts on inanimate surfaces

© Node Hingprakhon/Shutterstock.com

The active ingredient in bleach, sodium hypochlorite, is a broad-spectrum disinfectant as it denatures proteins and solubilizes cell membranes

© Alex Yeung/Shutterstock.com

Antibiotics

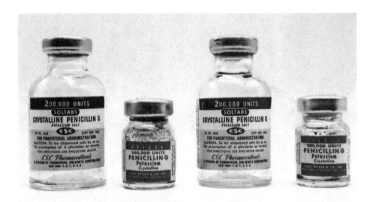

© Walter Cicchetti/Shutterstock.com

⌐ An antibiotic is a substance produced by one microorganism that kills or inhibits the growth of another microorganism. The mode of action of antibiotics includes; (1) inhibiting cell wall synthesis, (2) disrupting cell membrane function, (3) inhibiting protein synthesis, and (4) inhibiting nucleic acid synthesis. Antibiotics that are effective against a wide range of organisms, both Gram-positive and Gram-negative, are known as broad-spectrum antibiotics. Those antibiotics that work on a single taxonomic group are known as narrow-spectrum antibiotics. ⌐[1]

Testing of Antimicrobial Agents and Antibiotics

The filter paper disk diffusion method is used to determine the effectiveness of various disinfectants and antibiotics on the growth of bacteria. The filter paper disk method relies upon infusing the chemical and/or antibiotic into a filter disk and placing it onto an agar plate that contains a bacterium. ⌐ If the tested compound inhibits the growth of the bacterium, there should be a cleared zone around the disk (a **zone of inhibition**). The size of the zone of inhibition relates to the effectiveness of the chemical. After measuring the zone of inhibition, the organism can be classified as being Resistant (R), Intermediate (I), or Susceptible (S) to the agent being tested.

If the organism is susceptible, the antibiotic or disinfectant will inhibit the growth. This inhibition of growth can be because it has killed the organism (**bactericidal**) or because it is growth-inhibiting (**bacterio-static**). ⌐[1]

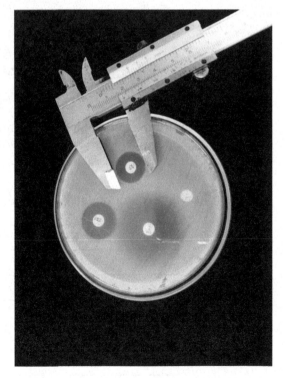

© Rossukon Sopak/Shutterstock.com

Testing the susceptibility of bacteria to antibiotic

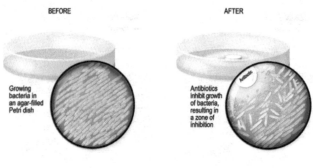

© Designua/Shutterstock.com

Did you Know?

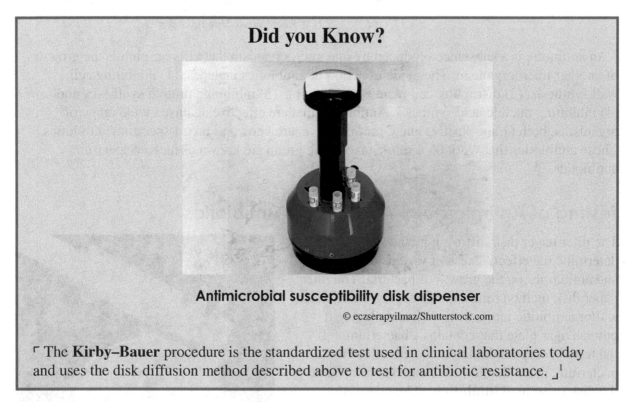

Antimicrobial susceptibility disk dispenser

© eczserapyilmaz/Shutterstock.com

┌ The **Kirby–Bauer** procedure is the standardized test used in clinical laboratories today and uses the disk diffusion method described above to test for antibiotic resistance. ┘[1]

Use the following Antibiotic Disk Diffusion Reference chart to help you with your lab today

Disk Symbol	Antimicrobial Agent
AM	Ampicillin
C	Chloramphenicol
CAZ	Ceftazidime
CB	Carbenicillin
CF	Cephalothin
CIP	Ciprofloxacin

(continued)

Disk Symbol	Antimicrobial Agent
E	Erythromycin
FOX	Cefoxitin
G	Sulfisoxazole
GM	Gentamicin
IPM	Imipenem
P	Penicillin
PB	Polymyxin
R	Rifampin
S	Streptomycin
SXT	Trimethoprim-Sulfamethoxazole
Te	Tetracycline
Va	Vancomycin

Exercise 13: Antimicrobial Compounds and Antibiotic Sensitivity

In today's lab, you will examine various disinfectants and antibiotics and their ability to inhibit bacterial growth. Species will be spread onto Mueller-Hinton agar plates for observation of zones of inhibition.

Objective(s)

1. To understand the difference between disinfectants, sanitizers, and sterilization.
2. To examine what agents are the most effective in limiting microbial growth.
3. Learn how to dispense antibiotic diffusion disks and spread plate cultures.
4. To know the role of various antibiotics and what cell features they target.

Materials Needed

1. Mueller–Hinton agar plates (number of plates designated by instructor)
2. Culture tube containing *Staphylococcus aureus*
3. Culture tube containing *Pseudomonas aeruginosa*
4. Culture tube containing *E. coli*
5. Culture tube containing *Enterobacter aerogenes*
6. Antibiotic disks, assorted
7. Antibiotic disk dispenser
8. Inoculating loop
9. Bunsen burner
10. Glass spreader (or plastic spreader)

11. Disk blanks
12. Bleach disinfectant
13. Isopropanol (or ethanol)
14. Oregano oil

Procedure

1. Each Mueller–Hinton agar plate will be inoculated with a single organism.
2. Using each bacterial culture, following the sterile transfer, places 2–3 loopful in the center of the agar place gently, without piercing the agar.
3. Then, sterilize the glass spreader by gently dipping in alcohol and passing through the Bunsen burner as performed in previous labs.
4. Once the glass spreader is cooled, use the spreader to evenly distribute the 2–3 loopful that were placed into the center of the agar plate.
5. Close the lid to the agar plate and allow it to dry for 3–5 minutes.
6. **For testing of disinfectants:** Using sterilized (ethanol-flamed) forceps, a sterile disk is picked up and dipped into the chemical agent being used. The disk is placed onto the agar surface and pressed firmly onto the agar.

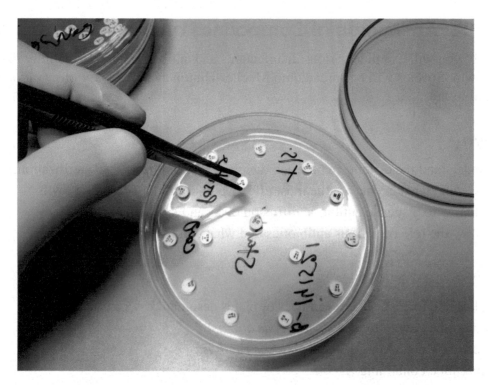

© Arif biswas/Shutterstock.com

7. For testing of antibiotics: Use the antibiotic disk dispenser. Instructions on how to use this tool will be provided by the instructor.

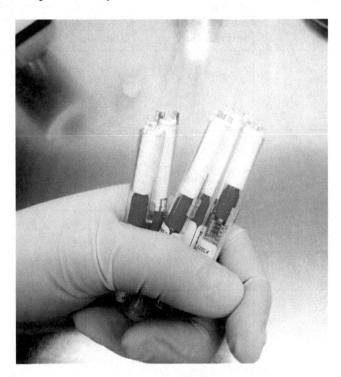

© TheBlueHydrangea/Shutterstock.com

8. Once complete with both disinfectant disks and antibiotic disks, place the plates in the incubator at 37°C for 18–24 hours.

Results

For all of the following tables, measure the diameter of the zone of inhibition (including the disk). Use a ruler and measure in mm. Also determine whether each organism is resistant (R) to an antibiotic, susceptible (S) to an antibiotic, or of intermediate (I) susceptibility to the antibiotic. Record your results.

Disinfectants

	Staphylococcus		Pseudomonas	
Disinfectant used and concentration	**Zone size**	**Resistant, Susceptible, or Intermediate**	**Zone size**	**Resistant, Susceptible, or Intermediate**

(continued)

Lab 13: Antimicrobial Compounds and Antibiotic Sensitivity   111

Disinfectant used and concentration	Staphylococcus		Pseudomonas	
	Zone size	Resistant, Susceptible, or Intermediate	Zone size	Resistant, Susceptible, or Intermediate

Disinfectant used and concentration	Escherichia		Enterobacter	
	Zone size	Resistant, Susceptible, or Intermediate	Zone size	Resistant, Susceptible, or Intermediate

(continued)

Disinfectant used and concentration	Escherichia		Enterobacter	
	Zone size	Resistant, Susceptible, or Intermediate	Zone size	Resistant, Susceptible, or Intermediate

Antibiotics

Antibiotic used	Disk Code	Staphylococcus		Pseudomonas	
		Zone size	Resistant, Susceptible, or Intermediate	Zone size	Resistant, Susceptible, or Intermediate

(continued)

Antibiotic used	Disk Code	Staphylococcus		Pseudomonas	
		Zone size	Resistant, Susceptible, or Intermediate	Zone size	Resistant, Susceptible, or Intermediate

		Escherichia		Enterobacter	
Antibiotic used	**Disk Code**	**Zone size**	**Resistant, Susceptible, or Intermediate**	**Zone size**	**Resistant, Susceptible, or Intermediate**

(continued)

Antibiotic used	Disk Code	Escherichia		Enterobacter	
		Zone size	Resistant, Susceptible, or Intermediate	Zone size	Resistant, Susceptible, or Intermediate

Questions

1. What conclusion can be made from these results? Does each disinfectant and antiseptic effectively kill or prevent the growth of each bacterium? Explain.

2. How does a bactericidal agent differ from a bacteriostatic agent?

3. How would you determine if a disinfectant or antiseptic is bactericidal or bacteriostatic?

4. What would explain why some disinfectants worked better than others? Why would certain species be more susceptible to different disinfectants?

5. What is a broad-spectrum antibiotic? Do any of the antibiotics used in this demonstration have a broad spectrum? Explain.

6. Which one of the organisms showed the most resistance to the antibiotics used?

7. Name the certain features of a bacterial cell that are targeted by antibiotics. Explain why each one is needed for bacterial cell growth.

Endnote

1. Adapted from *Techniques of Microbiology: A Laboratory Manual*, by Deborah A. Polayes. Copyright © 2021 by Kendall Hunt Publishing Company. Reprinted by permission.

LAB 14

Human Microbial Flora

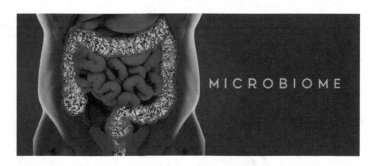

MICROBIOME

© Anatomy Image/shutterstock.com

Microorganisms are found on almost every surface on this planet: the soil, the air, the ocean, on human skin, and inside the body. The bacteria on your skin can be acquired temporarily by touching something such as a door handle in the bathroom. These bacteria are called transient flora because they can be easily removed from your skin by washing.

Other bacteria are intrinsically associated with your skin. These bacteria are called resident flora and are attached at the deeper layers of the skin, making them harder to remove even with vigorous washing. The normal resident bacteria generally do not do us any harm and may protect us from other bacteria.[1]

In this exercise, you will look at the natural flora found on your own skin, in your gastrointestinal tract (GI), and in your urinary tract!

NORMAL SKIN MICROFLORA

STREPTOCOCCUS VIRIDANS   STAPHYLOCOCCUS SAPROPHYTICUS   STAPHYLOCOCCUS EPIDERMIDIS

STAPHYLOCOCCUS HAEMOLYTICUS   CANDIDA   CORYNEBACTERIUM   PROPIONIBACTERIUM

PATHOGENIC SKIN MICROFLORA

STAPHYLOCOCCUS AUREUS   STREPTOCOCCUS PYOGENES   STREPTOCOCCUS PNEUMONIAE

KLEBSIELLA PNEUMONIAE   YERSINIA PSEUDOTUBERCULOSIS   YERSINIA ENTEROCOLITICA   PSEUDOMONAS AERUGINOSA

The human skin is home to many normal flora, these microbes along with natural barriers stop the growth of pathogenic microbes

© Juliasuena/Shutterstock.com

119

Intestinal bacterial flora

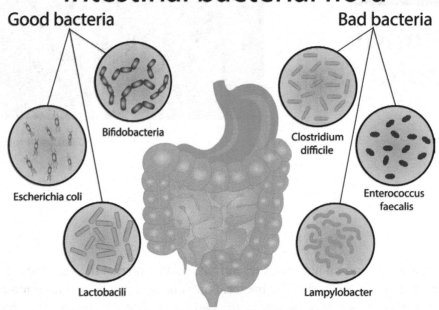

Good bacteria

Bifidobacteria

Escherichia coli

Lactobacili

Bad bacteria

Clostridium difficile

Enterococcus faecalis

Lampylobacter

Bacteria such as *Escherichia coli, Bifidobacterial*, and *Lactobacilli* are normal flora found in healthy GI tracts

© Olena758/Shutterstock.com

Urinary Tract Infection

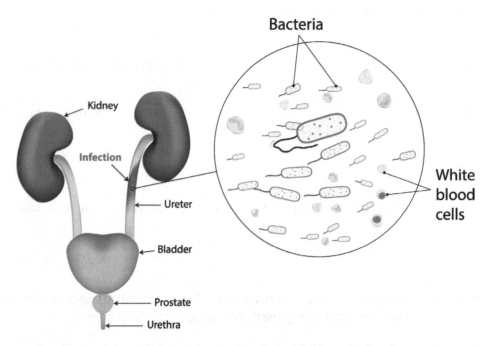

Bacteria

Kidney

Infection

Ureter

Bladder

Prostate

Urethra

White blood cells

For the most part, the urinary tract should be sterile, however, in the anterior urethra species such as *Staphylococci* and *Corynebacterium* can be found

© joshya/Shutterstock.com

┌ Many bacteria are found in the GI tract of humans. Most are normal inhabitants, but others are pathogenic and cause some serious illnesses. Normal flora usually includes the following groups: *Escherichia, Klebsiella-Enterobacter, Proteus, and Citrobacter*. Some of the pathogens usually encountered are; *Salmonella, Shigella*, and some strains of *E. coli*. As for skin, normal flora includes *Staphylococcus, Micrococcus, Corynebacterium, Brevibacterium, Dermabacter, and Malassezia*. These different genera are found in different locations depending on the oiliness or dryness of the skin location (i.e., armpit vs. sole of the foot). ┘² The Urogenital tract however should for the most part be sterile. Only in the distal portion of the urethra where contact with skin occurs can genera such as *Staphylococci* and *Corynebacterium* be found. Bacteria responsible for Urinary tract infections (UTI) include most commonly *E. coli* and *Pseudomonas aeruginosa*, the latter being an opportunistic human pathogen. The presence of bacteria in the urine is not considered a UTI unless there are more than 10^5. CFU (colony forming units) per mL.

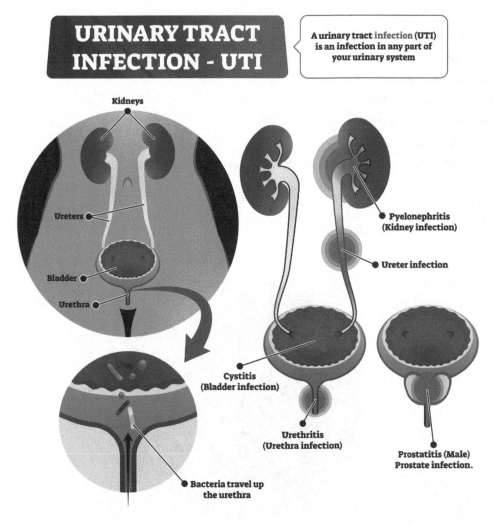

© VectorMine/shutterstock.com

Exercise 14: Human Microbial Flora

In this lab, you will swab areas that contain natural human flora. These collected specimens will be grown on selective and differential media in order to closely identify the unknown species as well as to gain knowledge of the microbiome of your body!

Objective(s)

1. Identify the microbiome of the human body.
2. Understand which selective and differential media are used to culture the bacteria of the skin, GI, and urogenital tract.
3. Know why specific microorganisms are found in certain areas of the human body.
4. Know which tests are used to determine infections caused by pathogenic bacteria in the GI, urogenital tract, and on the skin

Materials Needed

1. Sterile cotton swab
2. Mannitol Salt Agar plate
3. One vial of Saline
4. 2–3 MacConkey agar plates
5. 2–3 PEA-blood agar plates
6. One Pseudomonas Agar Plates
7. One Tube of sterile water
8. Urine specimen cup
9. Blood Agar plate
10. One culture tube each of *E. Coli, Proteus*, and *Pseudomonas*

Procedure

Part 1: Skin Bacterial Sample

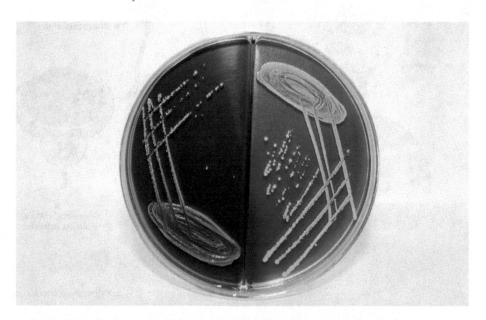

⌐ Salt mannitol agar plates are selective for salt-tolerant microbes such as those on your skin. It is also selective for mannitol fermentation (Yellow is positive for fermentation) as the pH indicator (phenol red) turns yellow in the presence of acids ˩[2]

© REJO JACOB JOSEPH/Shutterstock.com

1. Take a vial of saline and wet the cotton swab.
2. Press out the excess saline.
3. Rub the surface of the skin with a moist swab. (pro tip: Preferred areas to swab are the hands, elbows, feet, or the armpit. Also, a pus-filled sore might be nice!)
4. On a salt mannitol agar plate, gently rub the swab in ZONE 1 as if you were doing a streak plate.
5. Place the used swab in the red receptacle on the floor or the biohazard bag on the benchtop.
6. Then flame a loop and streak the inoculated section (ZONE 1) across the entire plate.
7. Seal the sides of the plate with tape (no one wants that to open on them!)
8. Place it in the INCUBATOR (37° C) NOT THE REFRIGERATOR with the lid side down. (Make sure your name/group name is on the plate[s])

Part 2: GI Tract Bacterial Sample

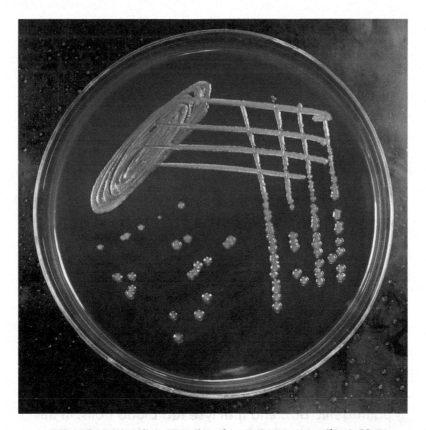

⌐ MacConkey is selective for Gram-negative. Pink colonies are a positive marker for lactose fermenting bacteria and white colonies are nonlactose fermenting

**Phenylethyl alcohol (PEA)-blood agar is
a selective medium for Gram-positive.
The active ingredient, PEA, inhibits the
growth of Gram-negative**

© Janeness/Shutterstock.com

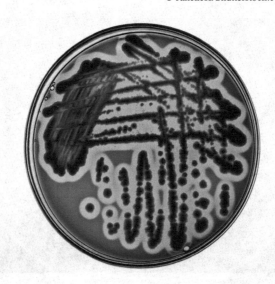

**PEA-blood agar can also show evidence of
pathogenic bacteria that lyse red blood cells. In this
image, the clearing behind each colony represents
beta-hemolysis, the complete destruction of red
blood cells** ⌋[1]

© Yayah_Ai/Shutterstock.com

1. Grab a vial of sterile water and a cotton swab
2. Grab one PEA-Blood Agar Plate and one MacConkey Agar plate
3. Go to the restroom to collect your individual sample. (pro tip: Save the cotton swab paper packaging sleeve to put swab back into when finished)

4. Wet the cotton swab with sterile water.
5. Then, swipe around the anus (butt hole) to collect the specimen on the cotton swab.
6. Streak the swab on both the PEA-Blood Agar plate and the MacConkey agar plate throughout the whole plate.
7. When finished, put the contaminated swab in the paper packaging sleeve and discard it in the red bag on the bench or the red receptacle on the floor.
8. Tape your plate and place it in the INCUBATOR (37° C) NOT THE REFRIGERATOR with the lid side down. (Make sure your name/group name is on the plate[s])

Part 3: Genitourinary Tract Bacterial Sample

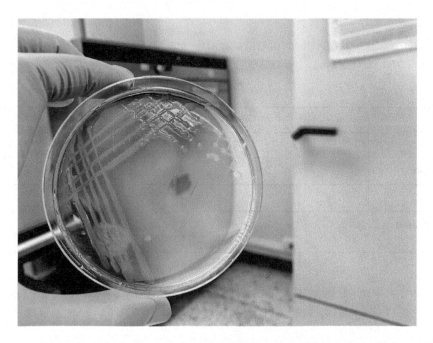

Pseudomonas aeruginosa produces a blue pigment (pyocyanin) when incubated on pseudomonas agar

© Pattikky/Shutterstock.com

1. Go to the restroom and urinate (pee) into a sterile urine cup. (pro tip: Don't fill it up! You only need 10 mL max [about ¼ full])
2. Come back to the lab and with a disposable pipette, and (0.5 mL) urine to the center of the plate. (Remember to double the CFU/mL when calculating the results)
3. Streak the urine onto the Pseudomonas, MacConkey, and Blood Agar plates using your inoculating loop.
4. Close the lid and tape your plate shut.
5. Place it in the INCUBATOR (37°C) NOT THE REFRIGERATOR with the lid side down. (Make sure your name/group name is on the plate[s])
6. Pour excess urine from sample cup down the toilet and put used cup in the red receptacle.

Part 4: Control Bacteria: *E. Coli, Proteus,* and *Pseudomonas*

1. Grab one MacConkey Agar plate and onePseudomonas Agar plate.

2. Divide the plates into three sections (like a pie) and label each section 1, 2, and 3 with a sharpie. (pro tip: Always write on the bottom of the plate, never on the lid)

3. Inoculate each plate with the bacteria in the following section: (Section 1) *E.Coli,* (Section 2) *Proteus,* and (Section 3) *Pseudomonas.*

4. Close the lid and tape your plate shut.

5. Place it in the INCUBATOR (37° C) NOT THE REFRIGERATOR with the lid side down. (Make sure your name/group name is on the plate[s])

Results

Part 1: Skin Bacterial Sample. Examining the salt mannitol agar plate choose colonies to record results

Mannitol agar

	Colony		
	1	2	3
Colony description			
Pigment			
Mannitol fermentation (+ or -)			

Part 2: Gastrointestinal Tract (GI) Bacterial Sample. Examining the MacConkey and Blood agar plates choose colonies to record results

MacConkey agar

	Colony			
	1	2	3	4
Colony description				
Pigment				
Lactose fermentation (+ or -)				

PEA-blood agar

	Colony		
	1	**2**	**3**
Colony description			
Hemolysis			

Part 3: Genitourinary Tract Bacterial Sample. Examining the Blood agar, MacConkey agar, and Pseudomonas agar plates choose colonies to record results

	Blood Agar	**MacConkey Agar**	**Pseudomonas Agar**
Number of Colonies			
Total Count (CFU/ml)			
Hemolysis			
Possible Coliforms Present			

Part 4: Control Bacteria: *E. Coli, Proteus,* and *Pseudomonas*

	MacConkey Agar	**Pseudomonas Agar**
E. coli growth description		
Proteus growth description		
Pseudomonas growth description		

Questions

1. What is a surgeon attempting to accomplish by using a 10 min scrub followed by an antiseptic rinse?

2. What is the difference between normal flora and transient flora?

3. What did you conclude about your skin microbial flora? Did you find colonies that could ferment mannitol? Explain.

4. What type of bacteria will grow on MacConkey agar? What is it selective for? What is it differential for? What is the color of lactose fermenting bacteria on MacConkey agar?

5. How is PEA-blood agar useful for clinical diagnosis? Is this media selective for any bacteria?

6. Based on the Blood agar MacConkey agar, and Pseudomonas agar plates used in the urine analysis were any colonies present? Based on all the results from the urinalysis would you consider the urine sterile? Explain.

7. If fecal coliforms or hemolysis were observed from your urine sample, where might these contaminants come from?

8. Why are females more prone to urinary tract infections than males?

Endnotes

1. Adapted from *Techniques of Microbiology: A Laboratory Manual*, by Deborah A. Polayes. Copyright © 2021 by Kendall Hunt Publishing Company. Reprinted by permission.

2. Adapted from *Laboratory Exercises in Microbiology,* by Keith E. Belcher. Copyright © 2012 by Kendall Hunt Publishing Company. Reprinted by permission.